ROCK IRON STEEL

The Book of Strength

STEVE JUSTA

IronMind Enterprises, Inc.
Nevada City, California

Rock, Iron, Steel: The Book of Strength
Copyright © 1998 Steve Justa

Cataloging in Publication Data
Justa, Steve—
Rock, iron, steel: the book of strength
1. Weightlifting   I. Title
1998   796.41   98-072725
ISBN 0-926888-07-2

Book and cover design by Tony Agpoon, San Francisco, California.
All photos courtesy of Steve Justa.

Published in the United States of America
IronMind Enterprises, Inc., P. O. Box 1228, Nevada City, CA 95959

Printed in the U. S. A. First Edition
10 9 8 7 6 5 4 3

I, the author Steve Justa, grew up in Nebraska in the small town of Harvard. I grew up on a farm and worked hard as a kid and played a few sports and always had an inborn drive to take everything to the limit that interested me in life. First it was dirt bike riding, not for competition in meets, but just around the farm

A self-portrait of the author.

and down on the little Blue River. I'd ride these motorcycles all the time, day and night. Then I really got into basketball. I'd practice all the time for years. Then it was partying and chasing the ladies.

I really never even knew how to lift weights until I got out of high school. I guess I was 18 years old when I started lifting seriously. Everything I've learned was self-educated. I've read enough books and magazines about lifting to make a stack clear to the ceiling, but that still wasn't good enough for me—I had to experiment and try to come up with my own ideas as well as try everybody else's. I've lived, eaten, breathed, and thought about lifting now for 20 years. So when I tell you something, it is coming from experience.

It all started when I was very young. I went to a rodeo in Burwell, Nebraska, when I was 10 years old, and I was sitting in the grandstand and looked up and saw a guy with big, powerful-looking arms, and I said to myself, "I want to be like that some day." And that's where it all started for me.

Steve Justa walks with huge weights on his shoulders, so he had to build something up to the task.

CONTENTS

About the Author   iii
Introduction   2
    Philosophy of Strength
Chapter One   6
    Lifting for Strength and Endurance
Chapter Two   14
    Carrying Weight
Chapter Three   20
    Dragging or Pushing Weight:
    G-Force Training
Chapter Four   26
    Power Aerobic Isometrics
Chapter Five   38
    Running with Weight
Chapter Six   42
    Singles Build Tremendous Strength
Chapter Seven   50
    The Hand and Thigh Lift
    or the Quarter Deadlift
Chapter Eight   56
    The Back Lift
Chapter Nine   62
    Partial Movements
Chapter Ten   70
    The Shovel or Pitchfork Lift
Chapter Eleven   74
    Barrel Lifting
Chapter Twelve   80
    Training Philosophy and Attack Plan
Chapter Thirteen   96
    Gaining Strength at any Age
Chapter Fourteen   100
    Personal Lifting Records

Other IronMind Enterprises, Inc. publications:

- *SUPER SQUATS: How to Gain 30 Pounds of Muscle in 6 Weeks* by Randall J. Strossen, Ph.D.
- *The Complete Keys to Progress* by John McCallum, edited by Randall J. Strossen, Ph.D.
- *IronMind®: Stronger Minds, Stronger Bodies* by Randall J. Strossen, Ph.D.
- *Mastery of Hand Strength* by John Brookfield, foreword by Randall J. Strossen, Ph.D.
- *MILO: A Journal for Serious Strength Athletes*, Randall J. Strossen, Ph.D., Publisher & Editor-in-chief
- *Powerlifting Basics, Texas-style: The Adventures of Lope Delk* by Paul Kelso
- *Of Stones and Strength* by Steve Jeck and Peter Martin
- *IronMind Training Tablet No. 1* by Randall J. Strossen, Ph.D.
- *IronMind Training Tablet No. 2* by Randall J. Strossen, Ph.D.
- *Sons of Samson, Volume 2 Profiles* by David Webster

To order additional copies of *Rock, Iron, Steel: The Book of Strength* or for a catalog of IronMind Enterprises, Inc. publications and products, please contact:

IronMind Enterprises, Inc.
P. O. Box 1228
Nevada City, CA 95959
tel: (530) 265-6725
fax: (530) 265-6725
website: www.ironmind.com

Philosophy of Strength

I will start by giving you some background about myself. First of all, that is me in the photographs. I am a believer in hard work; I've worked hard all of my life. And to get what you want out of life, you've got to think hard and work hard. It won't come overnight, but if you keep after it, it will come sooner or later no matter what it is you're after.

For example, a famous painter once painted a picture in five minutes and sold the picture of over $10,000; then someone asked, "How could a picture painted in such a short time be worth so much money?" The painter told him it may have taken only five minutes to paint that picture, but there was twenty years of hard work and countless hours of practice behind that five minutes of work, same as there would be for a heavy deadlift or squat or any other lift you want to get good at.

When I was 22 years old, I weighed 180 pounds. By the time I was 27 and weighed 280 pounds, I'd put on 100 pounds of efficient, usable, coordinated muscle in five years. All the time, I held hard common labor jobs. I've never used steroids and never will. I inherited a fast metabolism, and before I started lifting, could eat a horse every day and never gain a pound, so this gives you an idea of what you and I can accomplish with hard work.

I moved 400,000 80-pound hay bales, I carried a 100-pound chain vest on my back for 12 hours a day a month straight, walking through buildings full of grain and scooping grain with this vest on. I've worked in a hide house, throwing 100 pound cow hides all day long. I lifted, cut, hauled, stacked, and dragged heavy logs all of one summer. Those were some of the jobs I've held, and the whole time I was lifting steel weights, big rocks, and round hay bales, and pushing cars.

I've carried a 500 pound barbell on my back for a quarter of a mile. I've carried a 350-pound rock for two city blocks. I've cheat reverse curled 280 pounds. I've lifted 1200 pounds off the squat rack. I've shouldered a 315-pound barrel full of rocks and carried it two city blocks. I've lifted 800 pounds off the squat rack and held it for two minutes. All of these lifts were performed without the aid of a lifting belt, or any other form of support, other than regular street clothes.

All of this is what led me to my philosophy of strength, which is: You can build your body in 1,000 different ways and can have a 1,000 different kinds of strength and endurance, but indirectly, every kind of strength interacts with the others to a certain extent. For example, if you took the strongest Olympic lifter, and let's say he can clean and jerk 570 pounds, and you were to enter him in a powerlifting contest against the strongest powerlifter, say someone who squatted 1000 pounds or deadlifted 870 pounds and benched 700 pounds, the Olympic lifters would lose the contest—even though he might have a fair showing, he would still lose the contest.

The same would hold true if the powerlifter tried to match the strength of the Olympic lifter in the clean and jerk—the powerlifter would make a fair showing, but would never match that of the Olympic lifter. This why I say there are a thousand different kinds of strength.

So what does this tell us? It tells us that to be strong or big, or big and strong, you've got to develop a philosophy of strength, because all strength is interrelated to a certain degree.

This can be done in two different ways. One is to specialize in one or two or three different lifts day after day, month after month, year after year, and push way past normal limits, until you're three times stronger in these lifts than you were when you started out. When you've done this for three to four years, the strength you gain from these lifts will flow over to the other lifts you've never practiced and will virtually make you strong at something you've never practiced. Thus, you have the interrelation of strength.

The other way is to pick out 20 different lifts and always be doing something different every day. In this way, the strength from one lift flows into the other lifts a little bit at a time, and you never get bored because you are always doing something different. This is my philosophy.

Remember, consistency and momentum are the keys to success in the world of super strength. As it is in any pursuit, aim high with your goals and keep chipping away at the rock. Think of every workout you go through as a little chip off a big rock, and when you get that rock whittled down to nothing, you'll know you've been someplace. In the art of super strength, you must think in terms of years, not months or days. And have fun along the way. Don't get upset or discouraged if you fail to move a certain weight a certain number of reps. *The main thing to think about is doing what you can do. Don't worry about what you can't do.*

This gets back to what I said about staying within your limits. For example, say that two days ago you did 10 reps with 300 pounds in the deadlift, so you're thinking in your mind that you should be able to do 11 reps today. So you give it hell and you just barely get eight reps. You expected to get 11 and you only got 8. Now stop right here and let's examine this phenomenon.

In an amateur's mind, he or she will be thinking, "I did 10 reps with 300 two days ago and after all that hard work I should have gotten strong enough to get 11 reps with 300 today, but all I did was 8 reps. What's going on?" Then the amateur is mad at himself, thinking he's getting weaker instead of stronger, and is ready to throw the whole routine out the window, thinking, "This routine stinks and it isn't working. I've got to do something different."

Whereas in a professional lifter's mind, he thinks, "Huh, got eight reps" and doesn't give it another thought and proceeds on through his workout having fun. The difference with the professional is that he went through that years and years ago and knows it means nothing in the long haul.

See, the professional lifter knows all that he has to do is keep lifting consistently and the strength will come. The professional knows that no matter what workout he does, it will work eventually. The professional knows that doing what you can do is more important than doing what you've done or not doing what you think you should have done. The professional lifter knows and has confidence and knows if he does his best, strength will come to him. The professional knows in two weeks from now, he might be getting 15 reps with 300 no problem, no sweat mentally.

This kind of attitude is truly what separates the men from the boys, not just in lifting, but in all areas of life. There is no secret routine, there is no magical number of reps and sets. What there is, is confidence, belief, hard work on a consistent basis, and a desire to succeed. This is what I mean when I say accept your limits and when the time is right, you will push right through your limits time and time again, mentally and physically.

And as of this writing, I, the author of *Rock, Iron, Steel: The Book of Strength*, performed a one-quarter deadlift, or as the old-timers called it, the hand and thigh lift, with an unofficial weight of 2050 pounds a few inches off the floor. As far as I know, the previous record was around 1900 pounds, so I believe I own the unofficial world record. I am very proud of this and have been lifting for around 17 years now, and have worked hard to achieve the level of strength I possess, and I feel I've earned it and paid my dues.

Also, with this book, I try to touch the surface with tips and hints that will greatly accelerate your progress. And as with all areas of life, nobody knows it all. I found myself learning something new about the art of super strength practically every day. So always keep an open mind and maybe you, the reader, will be teaching me a thing or two about strength one of these days. And to all my fellow lifters out there, whether you're lifting 50 pounds to 1,000 pounds, I respect the hell out of you because you truly are warriors.

CHAPTER 1

Lifting for Strength and Endurance

Building and toughening the mind and will power. Conquering fear. Going to a place where you've never gone before physically and mentally. Building belief and confidence in one session, when you are in the mood to push your limits beyond what you've ever experienced. Tremendous work output. Setting a massive goal and accomplishing that goal in one day. These are some of the things an endurance-strength lifting session could give you.

Have you ever wondered what it would have been like to build the pyramids of Egypt? Have you ever wondered how tough mentally and physically the pyramid builders were? Have you ever wondered if you could have handled it? Pounding on massive blocks of rock all day long, cutting and shaping them with hammer and chisel, or dragging blocks that weighed tons, hundreds of miles with ropes by hand.

Or have you ever wondered what it would be like to compete in an Iron Man triathlon? I mean, have you ever been curious inside, if you really had to, could you run 25 miles, bike 100 miles, and swim 2-1/2 miles all in the same day? If you've never done it before, I bet if you really think about it and imagine you're really going to try to do it, just the thought of it would send fear and adrenaline through your veins.

Are you tough enough? If you've never done any kind of endurance training, chances are the thought of building pyramids by hand or doing an Iron Man competition will scare the hell out of you. And even the name—*Iron Man Triathlon*. Why do they call it the Iron Man when they don't even lift a weight?

Well, I think we all know the answer to that. Because any test of endurance training is a true test of intestinal fortitude, mental and physical toughness, and true will power and grit. People fear all kinds of things, but all fear stems from the doubt in one's own ability to conquer one's own mind. As Franklin D. Roosevelt said, "the only thing we have to fear is fear itself," and fear isn't real—it's just imagined in your mind because you let your mind stray; and if you can't control your mind, it will control you.

Now what I'm getting at is strength-endurance training. This kind of training not only toughens the body, it toughens your mind or, let's say, your will because your will is what steers your mind. And the stronger you make your will power, the easier all your regular lifting workouts will be. This strength endurance training is so powerful a tool that just one of these three- to five-hour sessions will stick with you mentally your whole life. It will leave such an impact on you it is truly unbelievable. It will forge such a picture way down deep in your mind, you'll never be able to forget it. Because when you're fighting for survival and fighting your mind with your will, and pumping the poison out of your pores and pumping the blood and fear and doubt and all this through your veins under all these pulls and tugs, positives and negatives, all condensed in a five-hour period, you will never ever forget it. I recommend that every lifter do this kind of training at least once in his life.

And now let's talk about this kind of training—strength-endurance training. Let me start out by telling you a story of what happened to me once. I'd been lifting for 10 years and was getting pretty good at a lot of lifts and was thinking I was getting pretty tough, which I was, BUT . . . one day when I'd been working in this foundry, a place where they made steel well head casings and a lot of other steel and iron pieces, the boss walked up to me and moved me to a different job because the guy that usually did this job had called in sick. The guy who called in sick was a small guy and probably didn't weigh 140 lb., and at the time I weighed 250.

Now I'd walked by his station quite a few times to get to my grinders station, so I'd seen him doing his thing quite a few times, but I never really gave it a second thought. That is, until the day was over and, after a 12-hour shift, that was all I thought about and until this day I still think about it quite a bit. But here is a description of what happened.

The new job I had to do was this: These steel couplers would travel down this conveyer belt from the foundry room and drop off on the ground at my station, and they were still pretty warm when I got them, and they would arrive one right after another all day long with about three minutes spacing in between each one.

Well, my job was to pick each one up with one hand and hit it with a 10-pound short hammer with the other hand and bang on it with the hammer to knock the hot sticky core sand out of it. The pieces varied in weight—some were 150 lb., but some weighed as much as 250 lb. and 300 lb., then you had to pick them up with two hands and shake the loose sand out. Well, sometimes that sand was pretty stubborn, and you'd end up picking each piece up 10 to 15 times, hammering, shaking and dropping, and rolling it around, and hammering and shaking, and dropping. If you took too long, you'd have a couple of pieces off the conveyer belt backed up on you already, and if you got too far behind, it was pure hell to catch up again. Each piece had quite a bit of heat resonating up from it, and you were constantly in a bent over, round back position.

Needless to say, after a couple of hours of this I was a wreck, physically and mentally, and I kept seeing a picture in my mind of the guy who usually did this job. He was skinny as a rail and he never even worked a sweat up when he was doing this job. He made it look easy. And here I was, thinking I was twice as strong as this guy was, but he made this job look easy. But here I was now, with it kicking my ass.

After about four hours, my whole outlook toward this little guy had undergone a metamorphosis. I found that this guy had to have about 15 to 20 times more endurance strength than I had, to do this job so easily day after day, week in and week out. And I suddenly realized why he only weighed 140 lb. I lost 10 lb. the first six hours, and my shift was only half over; sweat was running off of me like a river, and my muscles and tendons and ligaments were all on fire. That little guy was twice the lifter I was in my mind at that point. And I had a new found respect for him, not that I ever did not respect him, but now I really respected him because I knew how hard he was working.

Then I thought to myself, what good is it to be strong if you can't summon the strength over and over again. This is where endurance lifting comes in. Right then and there I made my mind up that I had to make myself tougher, mentally and physically. I was embarrassed to myself. There was nobody else around but me

Barrel lifts for reps are a surefire way to build endurance.

in that room, but the feeling of embarrassment still hit me like a ten-ton truck. I gutted the day out and went home and slept like a baby that night and was sore for about a week.

After that day at work I always told myself that every so often I would throw in some crazy form of endurance lifting once a month or once every couple of months or once every two weeks, whatever I was in the mood for. See, this little guy taught me the lesson of my life: There is more to being an "iron man" than how much weight you can lift for a few reps, or a max, or a workout of five sets of five or five sets of ten.

When it comes to being a true man of iron, in my opinion, you should be able to do 40 to 50 sets or 80 to 100 sets of a moderately heavy weight, not to the point of huffing and puffing, but to the point where you can do a movement over and over and over again for three to five hours, if called upon. Of course, take adequate rest in between sets, but not very much rest, and use sets where you're *just slightly tired* at the end of them.

To become a true iron man, this kind of training is critical once in a while. I'd recommend once every two months or once a month. Just one of these crazy workouts will stick with you the rest of your life mentally, and I believe even physically, because when you do something like this once, you know you can do it again some day even if you don't train for it. It'll build you a toughness that will stick with you the rest of your life.

Once I saw a guy do eight reps with 500 lb. in the bench press at a seminar, and he was huffing and puffing 30 minutes later on the microphone. In my mind, sure he did eight reps with 500 lb. in the bench, which was great, but his endurance strength was so low it took him 30 minutes to get his wind. Now, how much good is strength like that going to do you in real life survival situations without any endurance? I considered this guy weak physically and mentally after I saw this even though his bench was more than what I could do. Just like that little 140-lb. guy would have thought of me that day in the foundry if he could have seen me struggling.

I'd be willing to bet that I could have gotten *more reps* with *80%* of my max in a three-hour period than that bench presser could have gotten in three hours using just *40% of his max* even though his bench was, say, a max of 600 and mine was a max of 400. What's 40% of 600? Let's just make a rough estimate and say 250 lb.; and what's 80% of 400? Let's just say 325. Now, if I bench 325 for more reps in three hours than he does 250, tell me who is capable of more usable work output in a three-hour period. This is just another example of the benefits of strength endurance.

Look back at guys like John L. Sullivan, the old-time bare-fisted boxer around 1900. Guys like him used to fight bare-knuckled 60 to 80 rounds and drink 100 shots of whiskey the night before the fight and not give it a second thought. A lot of today's athletes are so pampered in my opinion, it is pathetic. They have lost sight of what it means to truly be a man or woman of iron. But that is where I come in. I'm here to remind the people who read this and at least bring this phenomenon back to light.

To do strength endurance, I would recommend a weight of about 50% or 60% of your max of an exercise that hits your whole body, and do 80 sets of three to six reps, or pick your favorite upper body exercise and do 40 sets and pick a lower body exercise and do 40 sets of it. After you work your upper and lower body that way, you'll still be getting 80 sets of three reps. Or you could do something like push a car for three miles, or drag a rock or carry a rock a mile with a lot of sets, or you can strap a weight vest on your back and walk five miles. Or you can do reps with weight. Use your imagination. Pick a goal and lift that. When you do get through it and accomplish it, you'll feel great about yourself. Like someone does when he finishes his first Iron Man Triathlon.

As an example, I once did 800 lb. in the quarter squat off a power rack for 100 sets of 20 reps. Each rep was up about three inches so I did 2000 reps. I moved 800 lb. the equivalent of 500 feet up in the air and 500 feet down, and I lifted a total of 1,600,000 lb. up three inches in three hours' time. One million six hundred pounds is equal in weight to 16 semi-truck and trailers fully loaded. Now, how's that for power and work load for one workout?

After I did this workout, my whole body felt like a rock for five days. After something like this, it might take your body a whole week to recuperate. But this also gives you time off to go on vacation or do your thing for three days; and believe me, you won't even feel guilty about not working out for a while because you'll feel you've earned it. This is also a good way to break the every-day monotony of training. Everybody loves a challenge, and be-lieve me, this kind of a workout will challenge anybody.

If you've never endurance-trained before, I challenge you to find out for yourself just how tough you really are. You will surprise yourself. Because once you've earned the right in your own mind to be able to look at yourself as an iron man or iron woman, nobody can ever take it away from you. Pick a weight you think you can do 2000 reps with, as I did. If you do 20 reps, it's 100 sets; if you do 10 reps, it's 200 sets; if you do five reps, it's 400 sets. This gives you an idea of the true grit I'm talking about.

When I did the 2000 reps for 100 sets of 20 off the power rack with 800 lb. in three hours, it was one of the hardest workouts of my life; and I didn't get much rest between sets either, maybe a minute or a minute and twenty seconds in between sets of 20 reps for 100 sets. Of course I didn't just jump into this level; I worked up to it. Remember, an Iron Man triathlete just doesn't jump in and finish a race like that with no training.

And, of course, the farther you move the weight with each rep, depending on the movement, the fewer sets and reps you will need to use. Say for example, you are doing the clean and jerk. Look how far you move a clean and jerk, maybe seven feet up each rep, compared to a deadlift, say two and one-half or three feet up. Remember, *the farther you move a weight and the faster you move it, the more work you are doing* so always keep this in mind.

Above all, no matter what I say about reps or sets or poundage percentages, you be your own boss and use your good common sense because everybody is different. We all have walked a different path to get where we are today, as well as lifted a different path—that's why everybody lifts differently, and why one routine works for one guy at the moment and not for another. To see where you're going, you've got to remember where you've been. This is as true in life as well as in lifting.

CHAPTER 2

Carrying Weight

Carrying weight is a true test of strength, whether it is a rock carried at waist or chest height, or a heavy piece of metal or engine block, or whether you're carrying a barbell across the shoulder, or a heavy log or pipe on your shoulder, or carrying behind both shoulders a barbell or anything heavy you can lift either from the ground or a stand and walk with. Walking with heavy weight builds tremendous endurance and strength and coordination, and I would include some sort of carrying lift in any workout I would be doing in the quest for super strength.

Goerner, one of the all-time great strongmen, stated the three tests to gauge a man's strength were: How much you can lift off the ground, how much you can put over your head, and how much weight you can walk with. Once Goerner strapped a 1440-lb. piano on his back and walked 50 feet with it. Now that's what I call strength. And another old-time strongman named Horace Barre carried a 1440-lb. barbell on his shoulder for six steps. Yet another old-time strongman named Louis Cyr loaded a 900-lb. rail from the ground to his shoulder and walked 50 feet. These three men were among the strongest men who ever lived, and they all practiced some form of carrying weight. And sooner or later you will probably come upon a situation in real life that involves carrying weight in some form or another.

I think being able to walk while carrying or supporting weight is a true test of strength, power, and coordination. In some of my own workouts once in a while when I really felt like taking things to the limit, I'd do 50 sets of carrying a heavy barbell on my shoulders. I'd carry it from one side of the road to the other. I had stands welded to the bar so all I had to do was drop my weight about four inches and it was resting safely on the ground. In some workouts I'd do this 50 sets in one workout, carrying over 700 lb.

each set across the road, and go for a total distance of over 1/2 mile to a mile. Sometimes in one workout I've carried 1200 lb. 20 to 30 steps without a belt, wraps, or lifting suit.

Once when it had been raining and I had a barbell set up in my backyard, a friend came over and I was showing off. I picked an 800-lb. barbell off the rack and carried it 50 feet through the mud—at times my feet were sinking in the mud up to my ankles—

Steve Justa shoulders and strolls with a railroad rail.

and set it on another rack. I just barely made it. It was a danger-ous, very dangerous stunt and a back and leg breaker, but I made it—just barely.

But this gives you an idea of what carrying weight can do for you. It builds practically every muscle in your body from your toes to the top of your head. It gets your ankles, shins, calves, thighs, front, back, side. It gets your hips, groin, rear end, side hip. It gets the front of your stomach, the side of your stomach, your lower and upper back, your shoulders, chest, hands, wrists, arms, and neck.

Walking with heavy weight is an all-around excellent movement especially for anyone who's interested in allover development
and who's interested in developing super strength. Basically that's
how the human body was meant to work and move—in a standing
position. Most human movement takes place in the standing position so it makes good sense to work all these muscles in the human
body from the standing position.

When carrying weights with a barbell behind the neck, a two-
inch solid steel bar made from cold rolled steel works the best,
because there is no bounce in the bar. It is rock hard solid and that
makes it a lot safer to walk with. It also works better for carrying
weight on the shoulders because there is more surface area on your
skin. You can build a stand that welds right to the bar so that
when you pick up the weight and the stand, you can set it right
back down on the ground when you are tired because when you lift
the weight and walk with it, the bottom of your stand is only about
four inches off the ground. Or you can set up two squat racks and
carry the weight from one rack to the other. Or take the weight
from one rack and carry it back to the same rack. You can carry
heavy barrels on your shoulder, or rocks at your waist, or barrels at
your waist or logs on your shoulder or a barbell at your waist, or
practically anything.

If all I did was carry for a workout to get the strongest the
fastest, I would do 10 sets of 20-step carries every day, and when
the weight you're using starts to feel light, ADD more. And rest a
few minutes in between each set. Use a weight that's just heavy
enough to make you just slightly winded at the end of each set. If
you're doing other lifts as well, I would just throw the carrying in
once or twice a week and do just two or three sets each workout
with about 20-step carries.

Chain or Weight Vest Carry

Walking with a heavy vest or pack builds super strength endurance. Once I wore a 100-lb. chain vest every day for eight to ten
hours a day for a month straight. I was wearing this vest while I
was walking through buildings full of corn. I was scooping the

corn and raking grain, and when I wasn't in the buildings full of corn, I was doing other duties for my day job. And once in a while I'd sit down and take a rest, but all in all, I carried that 100-lb. vest for a lot of hours.

I once did a two-mile hike with a 200-lb. chain vest without taking the weight off my back. That two-mile march with 200 lb. on my back took me 50 minutes. So, in other words, I had 200 lb. strapped and supported on my back for close to an hour without a rest, plus I walked a distance of two miles. I would have to say it was one of the hardest things I've ever done for one effort without a rest in my life. Sweat was running off me like a river and my whole body was shaking. After I made it the two miles and threw that vest on to the ground, it felt like 1000 lb. had been lifted off my shoulders. I could barely even walk across the street to sit down. When I did sit down, I sat there for half an hour before I even tried to get up. And when I did get up, I was still shaky. The next day every muscle in my body felt hard and tight.

See, I did this years after I had worn that 100-lb. vest at work scooping grain. It had been raining out, and the rest of my weights were outside in the mud, so I decided to test my strength walking with weight. I made it two miles, and it was tough, really tough. But that was because I just jumped into it. I didn't train up to it as I should have, and I hadn't done any vest work for over 10 years.

The point I want to make is that it took every ounce of will power, strength, intestinal fortitude, and bad attitude I could muster up to carry 200 lb. two miles without a rest. And I've had over 17 years of backbreaking training behind me.

If you want to build super strength and devote one year of your time, that is 40 to 50 minutes a day for a year straight, for example, you can start out with 20-lb. pack and walk two miles. Then the next day you do it again, only this time you ADD a pound and go two miles with 21-lb. pack; and you do this every day, ADDING just one pound every day, and you do this for a year straight. You'd be carrying 385 lb. on your back for two miles, and you probably wouldn't even be tired because you'd been doing it every day and your body would be used to it.

Now in just one year, you would have acquired super strength and super endurance and stamina. I see no reason in the world why your body should fail to be able to carry an extra pound every day over a two-mile distance. Right off hand, I don't know of anybody who has the strength and stamina to carry 400 lb. two miles in one effort without a rest. This is the potential of vest training or pack training.

Steve Justa sports his one-of-a-kind weight vest.

I remember when I carried that 100-lb. vest at work all day. After I did that for a month, I entered a team basketball tournament. The vest work I had done earlier really paid off because I was doing things out there on that basketball court I never could have done before that weight vest training. It was as if I were just inflicting my will upon everything I did out there.

The benefits of carrying weight for long distances are tremendous. The weight vest carry is a whole dimension in itself in the art of super strength. I remember in that basketball game, I was dribbling down the court, and this big 275'er planted on me, and I just ran him over like he wasn't even there. I'll bet he slid 20 feet backwards on his back after I ran over him, and this was surprising to me. That was a sure sign of the power that weight carrying can give you. Plus, I was doing jump shots and ball control in the air like I had never done before.

So, in the world of super athletes, this should be food for thought.

CHAPTER 3

Dragging or Pushing Weight: G-Force Training

   Dragging or pushing weight is an excellent way to build tremendous power in the body and tremendous endurance. Dragging weight is when you pull backwards, dragging a weight that is in front of your body back toward you as your body is moving backwards. Pulling or pushing a weight, which I call the same thing, is when you push a car forward, for example, with your hands or shoulder, or pull a car or sled forward using a shoulder harness or ropes as your body is moving forward. Dragging and pulling work different muscles.

   The sumo wrestlers of Japan drag weight and push weight all the time, and they possess some of the most formidable body power in the world. The sumos will drag tires up hills with a rope vest while another sumo is riding in the tire. And when they wrestle each other, they are always pushing against each other, using power in the toes, ankles, calves, shins, thighs, hips, hamstrings, back, stomach, chest, shoulders, arms, legs.

   I don't have any idea how much free weight a sumo wrestler can lift, but with the muscles they've developed, I bet most weightlifters would get the education of their lives if they climbed in the ring with a *Yokuzuma*, which is a champion sumo wrestler. The weightlifter, if he were good, would probably outlift the sumo in a weightlifting contest. But when it came to using the muscles the sumo trained every day, he would probably outclass the weightlifter. So it is good to throw this kind of training in your routine once in a while to develop that all-around usable strength.

I myself once pushed a four-ton truck four city blocks without stopping to rest, and one of those blocks was uphill slightly. Pushing and dragging cars and trucks with a vest or harness will give you a certain kind of strength other routines won't; or dragging a weighted sled or tire filled with concrete, or even just a plain tire if you sprint or run, will be a tremendous workout.

There was an old-time wrestler who used to pull a one-bottom plow through the field with a harness, and he was virtually undefeated as a wrestler. I think one of the best ways to drag weighted sleds is with football-cleated shoes on, dragging the sled through the dirt. I would make the sled out of cold rolled one-inch steel bar in a V-shape, and at the front of the "V", I would mount a skid plate to keep the front from digging in. I would build some sort of a harness out of those straps they use to tie semitrailer loads down with. That webbed strap is super strong and it is pretty wide, too.

Then I would use a chain or a thick rope from the harness to the sled and for the workout I would drag a certain amount of weight a certain distance every day, say maybe one city block either in one set or multiple sets, and I would go the same distance every day. Then, as I got stronger, I would start adding weight to the sled. Use anything you can think of for weight for the sled; use your imagination—you'll come up with something.

Pushing cars and trucks builds your arms, shoulders, chest, stomach, hips, front thighs, calves, and toes. Dragging cars or trucks builds your front shins, biceps, back, hamstrings, toes, and ankles. So I would drag that weight sled also as well as pulling it. I would mix dragging and pulling, and pushing and pulling forward, as well as dragging sideways, and dragging sideways around in circles with a scissors step. The scissors step is when you go sideways, you place one leg across and in front the other leg one step, then place that leg across and behind the other leg the next step, all the time moving sideways and repeating this, front and back.

Dragging sideways will work muscles you never even knew you had, and it gives you a lot of power in the hips and side of your legs. Sometimes drag things behind you with one arm as your body is going straight ahead, sometimes with two arms; sometimes drag with one arm around in circles or sideways, sometimes with two arms; and sometimes drag backwards with one arm, sometimes with two arms.

Push cars or trucks with your hands or shoulders; you can even push against trees if you like—the sumos of Japan do this. I call it G-force training. For example, they'll stand in front of a telephone pole and smash their palms into the pole for an hour straight, rotating their hands. They probably use 25% power each hand smash, but when you do it for 20 minutes to an hour, this method builds great strength. They'll do the same with their legs except they will pick their legs up one at a time and drive them into the ground. Sometimes they'll do this a thousand times a leg every day.

See, what makes this method build strength is the sudden stop. When the leg or hand comes to the sudden stop, the G-force that is generated starts building strength. The same effect can be gotten by jumping off a small block or step with both legs about 50 times in a row, or putting a shoulder into a brick wall sideways about 50 to 100 times each side. It is a rush and gives you a kind of strength you'll never forget. I brought it up because it also builds speed strength and stopping strength, and is great for fighting skills. The sumos also mix this kind of training in with their pushing and dragging routines.

If you're jumping off steps or stands, and you've been at a certain height step for a couple of weeks, after a while I would start jumping from higher and higher steps. The higher the step you jump from, the more impact you hit with, and to survive that impact takes great strength. But if you progress slowly just like with weightlifting, you shouldn't have any trouble at all with injuries. And, who knows, maybe you'll build the strength to jump from a 20-foot high roof, land flat on your feet, knees slightly bent, and do it as easily as the average person would jump from the curb to the street.

A good all-around G-force training program would be 50 sumo leg stomps, 25 each leg. Do this by standing on one leg; bring your other leg as high as you can, lean your torso forward and drive your leg that's in the air smashing into the ground. Then switch legs and do the same thing with your other leg. Use about 50% of your power until you get well-practiced. The tougher you get, the harder you'll smash the ground. Do 50 reps, then move on to palm smashing into a wall or tree.

With elbows bent, stand close to the tree or wall and smash your palm into the tree or wall. Use about 50% of power to start, then the stronger you get, the stronger you hit. Do 50 reps, 25 each hand. I would recommend wearing a thick pair of leather gloves.

After leg stomps and palm smashes, do:

• 50 wall or tree kicks, straight on, with leg straight, waist-high, 25 each leg

• 50 straight arm smashes, at arm's length, palm smashing against tree or wall straight ahead of body

• 50 reps wall or tree side kicks; stand on one foot, kick straight out to side, bending torso forward

• 50 shoulder smashes into wall or tree; tense shoulder and smash into wall sideways with shoulder

• 50 jumps from elevated platform or stairs to ground, using narrow and wide stance, 25 each, with torso leaning forward; the tougher you get, the higher you jump from

• 50 palm side smash on tree or wall; stand facing tree, arm straight in front of you, smash palm sideways into tree using chest to pull arm into tree. Do 50 of these.

This whole workout will leave your body feeling like a rock when you're done. If all you do is the G-force workout, I would recommend you do this once every three days the first week, then once every two days the second week and then once every day the third week, for the ultimate in physical perfection. Then go back to once every three days the fourth week, once every two days the fifth week, and once every day the sixth week, and so on. This cycling and spaced rest lets your body attain its strength and peek stamina.

Pushing, dragging, and pulling weight, and G-force training will give you power and strength in muscles that no other form of training does as directly. Like the hand smash into a telephone pole, when done for an hour straight in a slow rhythmic pace that doesn't tire you out too fast, it will make your whole upper body feel like it's been chiseled out of granite. If you can jump off a 2-foot high step 200 times in a row without stopping, your legs will feel as though they're on fire.

Isometrics and G-force training will give your body a feeling like it's probably never known before; you'll feel like a machine. Dragging, pushing, or pulling weight with one hand or two won't give you a spectacular feeling like isometrics or G-force training will, but it will give you strength and power in places you've never had them before.

CHAPTER 4

Power Aerobic Isometrics

What is the art of speed or the ability to move the body quickly? What does it take to develop speed? I believe it is the ability to tense your muscles very powerfully and release muscle fiber at a very fast rhythm, as well as having very strong ligament and tendon strength to hold the body together once it gets going. So the more tensely you can contract all your muscles clear down deep to the bone, the more speed you should be able to generate, once you learn to coordinate all the muscles into play for any certain movement. So what you want to do is make your whole body feel more or less like a steel shaft, every part tensely and tightly connected to every other part.

Wind and endurance play a big role too. Nothing on the planet builds strength or the ability to support and move heavy objects better than lifting free weights. On the other hand, nothing on the planet builds speed strength, or the ability to move the body quickly, faster than power aerobic isometrics combined with the practice of the actual movement you want to get speed in, plus the use of free weights. The isometrics pull it all together, making everything work together for the total speed-strength package.

Of course, the faster you can move your body, the more power you generate. So let's give you an example of upper body speed — Bruce Lee. It is said that Bruce Lee possessed some of the fastest hand speed the world has ever seen. I guess he was so fast that for a lot of the movie scenes he shot, he had to slow his punches down by 30% of what he was capable, because if he didn't, he was so fast on camera that the people wouldn't have even been able to see him throw the punch. Now that's what I call speed strength!

I read that Lee had a two-inch punch that could knock the wind out of a 250-lb. man and knock him off his feet and backward ten feet. Now that's speed and power! Here's a quote from Bruce Lee himself—a simple statement, and it was this: "The less effort, the more power." This is so true, especially when it comes to moving the body with speed.

In weightlifting this philosophy works also, but is very dangerous, because your muscles have the ability to rip your tendons and ligaments right off their attachment points. An example is the 60-year-old lady who never lifted a weight in her life, when scared to death, lifts a car off somebody pinned beneath the car with pure adrenaline flow. This is another good example of the less effort the more power. She didn't think about whether she could lift that car or not in her state of mind; she just did it, with no effort.

I believe the best way to open up this natural channel of "less effort, more power" as far as moving the body with speed is the use of power aerobic isometrics.

Let's go back to Bruce Lee, the famous karate master. Bruce did things in his training like this: He would hold a five- or three-pound steel ball in his palm by his fingers with the palm down and his arm straight out in front of his body. That doesn't sound like much, which it isn't—anybody could do that, right? But here's the kicker: He'd do it for eight hours straight. When one arm got tired, he'd switch it to the other, and when that arm got tired, he'd switch back, and so forth. But the killer is, he'd do this for eight hours straight.

When you do something like this, even with a weight that light for long enough, eventually the whole body comes into play. You'll be pulling from the toes to the top of your head after eight hours of this, and the effect it will give you is that your whole body—and I do mean your whole body—will feel like a steel shaft, like it is all one unit of rock-hard strength.

Now this is the basis for speed strength training. But there's no reason to get this radical and, besides that, nobody has the time to devote to this man-killer training. But I have the answer to where you can get the same results in one-tenth of the time, and this is power aerobic strength isometrics. This kind of training works the muscles from the inside out, whereas lifting weights and such works the muscles from the outside in. Now, you're probably saying to yourself, "is this guy off his rocker, or what?" But, take my word for it, I know what I'm talking about because I've lived it. A little later I'll tell you just how to do these isometrics.

Bruce Lee knew the secret of speed strength, and he was a master of his art. When it comes to fighting and quickness afoot, and burning fat off the body and feeling super light and super quick on your feet, these isometrics are the way to go. I don't know if it's true or not, but I read Bruce Lee worked up to a point where he could take an 80-lb. dumbbell with one hand and hold it straight out in front of his body, shoulder height and parallel with the floor, and hold it there for three minutes. This is what I would call super strength and power without the size, because I think Bruce only weighed 150 lb. soaking wet.

Now let me tell you my own experience with isometrics. When I was about 21 years old, I got a job with a custom hay bale hauler. And all the work was done by hand and a hay hook. The first day on the job I was helping my boss load hay from a barn hayloft up by Lincoln, Nebraska, in December. It was cold out that day, and I was fired up about my new job because I knew it would be tough, and that's the way I wanted it.

My boss was exactly one year older and about 70 to 90 lb. lighter in bodyweight than I. And he had been doing this kind of work since he was ten years old. Well, I'll never ever forget the sight of his arms when he took his shirt off about five minutes into the job. Here it was about ten degrees out, wind howling and snow flakes blowing around. He took his jacket off in this weather and had a short-sleeved T-shirt on, working out in that half-blizzard. But the sight that to this day still sticks in my mind, when he stuck that 100-lb. hay bale with his hay hook and curled it up to his chest with one arm, is the rock-hard chiseled veins in his bicep and forearm. The veins looked as if they were carved into a piece of granite as they stuck out. His arm density was unbelievable. Since that time I've read enough bodybuilding books and powerlifting books and Olympic lifting books to fill up a room. And not one person's picture I've ever seen in all these books had the arm density that my boss had at that point in time. I think the best arm for muscular vascularity and density was Frank Zane's in his prime,

and his arm didn't even come close to what my boss's arm ̄
like. If you've never seen anything like it, you can't describe
saw it, and I still can't describe it. My boss could do ten one-a
pullups and tell you jokes the whole time.

Steve Justa demonstrating an isometric deadlift.

That first day was when I also got my education. For anybody
that has never custom hay bale hauled for a living using a hay
hook, let me say it takes strength, balance, coordination, speed,
concentration, eye coordination with your feet and hands, and a lot
of isometric strength, wind, and intestinal fortitude along with a

rong mind to do this for a living. Yeah, I remember that first day o well; I've never been so humiliated in all my life. Have you ever heard the old line when the body goes, the mind goes with it. You'd better believe it. That's why boxers have to train so hard. When your body tires or is uncoordinated and to make matters worse you have to think about what you're doing when you are just fighting to survive, let me tell you, that's when the s--- hits the fan.

Have you ever noticed that when somebody is a professional at what they do, they always make it look so easy, like it takes practically no effort at all. That's because to a professional, it is easy and practically doesn't take any effort at all to them, physically or mentally. A professional doesn't even have to think about what they do—they just do it. It's like the 60-year-old lady lifting a car off a kid, or Bruce Lee's statement "the less effort the more power." It all goes hand in hand.

Well, that first day, I was working as hard and as fast as I could. I'd throw a hay bale and my hay hook would go flying with it. I'd step in cracks between the hay bales and fall down while I was dragging bales. I'd miss my spot where I wanted my bales to go and have to rearrange them five to six times to get it right. I was fumbling and stumbling and sweat was running off me like a river; I was sucking for wind. I was doing everything in my power just to survive and to look good in my boss's eyes. But what was really killing me was my boss was laughing and telling me jokes the whole time and getting twice as much work done as I was. And then he was asking me questions while I was in a state of total exhaustion and mental turmoil. Have you ever tried to answer somebody's questions when you're in this state of mind? Well, let me tell you, it is pure hell.

What's all this got to do with speed training? It all goes together: muscle tone and density, coordination, speed movements, more power with less effort. Hauling hay and doing it fast involves all these aspects, the same aspects you must have for speed strength.

After that first day on the job, my mind was spinning. I hauled hay for a year and was getting pretty good at it, but no where near the level my boss was at. Then I started to lift weights and haul hay. I'd haul hay for two to three hours a day, actual physical labor time. The rest was riding in the truck. Then I'd come home and lift weights. I did lifts like the deadlift, squat, clean and jerk, and bench press and rock lifting.

Here are what my lifts were during the time period of my second year of hay bale throwing: my bench was 180, my deadlift was 300, my clean and jerk was 180, my squat was 225, and I was rock lifting a 200-lb. rock. I kept hauling hay and lifting, and two years later I was still hauling hay, and my lifts then went up to carrying a 350-lb. rock. I was deadlifting 500, benching 315, clean and jerking 300, and squatting 450 or 500. But the point I want to make is that I doubled my strength in weight lifting, so you'd think that my hay hauling, from all my increased strength in the weights—a double in strength with the weights, was twice as easy also. WRONG. All this increase in strength with free weights made my hay hauling *maybe* 10% easier *at the most*.

But my fourth year hauling hay, I tossed the weights to the side and did nothing but isometrics. After hauling hay, I'd come home and do an hour or two of isometrics every night. I did hundreds of different positions of pushes, pulls, one-handed, two-handed; side overhead squats, squat twist—about every direction you could think of, from every angle.

First, I built a power rack. I used two I-beams, one on each side, and I cut holes in the I-beam about two inches apart from bottom to top in each beam. The beams were about eight feet tall. Then I put the beams in a frame so I could use a pipe that slides in and out of the beams to connect them, and I could adjust this pipe to any height I wanted so that I could do deadlifts, squats overhead, one-arm overhead pushes, one-arm side deadlifts, etc.

I came up with hundreds of movements, different pushes and pulls, and over half of these could never be performed with weights. That is one of the great things about isometrics: You can work muscles, joints, tendons and ligaments that it would be virtually impossible to work with free weights. On some exercises, I pulled as hard as I could for seven seconds; others I held for two minutes, and others I held for five minutes; I just kept mixing it up. Sometimes I'd do the same exercise 50 sets for seven-second holds; other times I'd do 50 to 60 different exercises for a one-second hold in the same workout.

Other times I'd do one-hand rotating like Bruce Lee did as I described earlier in this chapter, except I'd use about 50% output. I'd do these for an hour straight. Sometimes I'd use 30% of my max for the pulls or pushes that took over three minutes. On the shorter-timed pulls, I'd go 70% max to 90% max. I just kept experimenting. Everything I did on these isometrics, no matter what variation of workout, tremendously improved my speed strength, and muscle coordination and density.

My favorite advanced routine was this:

Day 1—Deadlift bar at knee height, do 50 sets of 5 second holds each set. Rest 30 seconds between each set. Pull at 80 to 90% of power each pull. Pull up on bar and try to twist bar to the left. Then on the next set, pull up on bar and try to twist bar to the right. Alternate between left and right each set until you get to 50 sets.

Day 2—Do between 30 to 50 different exercises in one work-out, working from my toes to the top of my head; one five-second hold at 90% max for each exercise.

Day 3—Choose 20 of my favorite exercises, and do one two-minute hold each exercise at about 40% of max pulling and push-ing power.

Day 4—Do three of my favorite exercises, say, full squat with upward twist left, then right, every other effort; one-half deadlift; and curl. Do 100 half-second bursts on each exercise at 90% max pulling power, five reps at a time, until I got to 100 reps each exercise, pacing myself to avoid fatigue.

Days 5 and 6—Rest.

Day 7—Do 30 sets of quarter-block sprints; rest 6 hours, then do a two-mile run.

Day 1—Start all over again.

This workout developed extreme muscle coordination and tensing endurance strength like rock climbers have to have. It gave me running strength and endurance. It gave me muscle strength and control in the little muscles and hit the tendons and ligaments in all different angles. It made me light afoot. It gives you the kind of strength essential to sports, because it allows you to transform your power into quick movement.

Another good workout is to choose 25 of your favorite exercises and do one three-second blast on each exercise, 90% of max, everyday, seven days a week, and do three half-block sprints and a half-mile run every day. The sprints and the run are optional, but the sprinting and running tie everything together as one unit, which is great if you're involved with sports.

Now, here's the kicker. I lifted weights for two years during my hay hauling and I doubled my bodily strength in weightlifting in those two years, and my hay hauling only got about 10% easier. After a few short months on the power strength aerobic isometrics, my hay hauling became 40% easier. The isometrics made me feel like a steel shaft. They burned the fat right out of the muscle from the inside out. They made my muscle super dense and super efficient. They gave me super-speedy quick movements. They made me feel light as a feather afoot. They gave me great endurance. Speed strength is the ability to tense muscles strongly, densely, and quickly in coordination, and that's what these isometrics (ISOs) will do for you.

The next time you're in the gym, stick an empty bar in the power rack in the upper squat position. Set the bar at a height where you can't get your legs straight in a quarter squat position, and then just push the bar up to the pins with your shoulders in the squat position, and push up with 40% of your power, pushing for three minutes, and then walk out and sit down and rest. Then get up and you will feel how these make you quick as a spark, and you'll feel how they burn the fat right out of the muscles almost instantly.

When doing any isometric movement, lock your whole body and work on tensing your whole body as one unit from head to toe. And, of course, the better you get and the more you practice with these ISOs, the easier they will become. Also remember, in any isometric movement you're pushing and pulling against immovable objects but your body does not move.

Isometrics are a must for anyone who wishes to gain bodily speed strength, or if you are a weightlifter or athlete or strongman or just an average man or woman off the street or in your house or

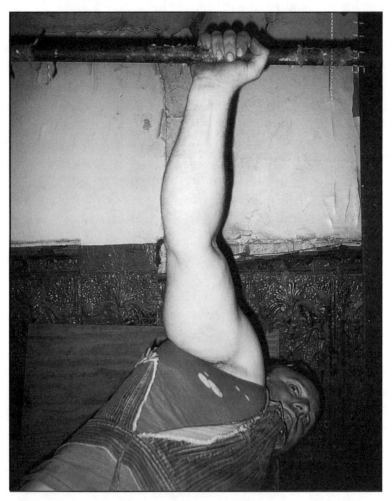

Steve Justa doing side press ISOs.

garage who wants to keep your weight down and have a beauti- fully built, strong, sleek, rock-hard build, with speed and coordina- tion. I'm telling you these aerobic isometrics will melt the fat right off your body virtually in one workout, especially if you do the one-minute to three-minute holds and work a lot of different exercises.

If you're a strength athlete with free weights and you want to keep making good gains with your free weights and add these isometrics, I would advise you to not spend over ten minutes' total time on these isometrics a day. If you do 30 to 40 minutes a day on these isometrics, you'll gain great speed strength, but lose strength in your free weights because it just takes too much out of your body—that is, unless you're at a really advanced level at doing both.

But, as I say, just grab something that won't move with one hand and try to pull it up and into your chest and lock all muscles and pull for two minutes and then release and rest, and you will feel instantly what these will do for you. No bull—you'll know instantly.

Now, to gain sprinter's speed I would do isometrics that mimic the way the body moves when it runs. As well as all other sports, I would do isometrics that correspond with the movements of that sport, as well as movements also that don't correspond with the sport for an all-around development.

Another advantage is when you do short isometric holds like one second to seven seconds. You can go through a whole 40-minute workout and feel fresher and better after you're done than before you started. You're making the muscle denser, and ligaments and tendons stronger and thicker, and you'll burn fat without tiring yourself out. What other form of exercise can you do where you feel fresher and better after you're done, and melt fat, and gain speed and muscle coordination, and get all these good benefits with virtually no exhaustion? That's what the short-second-hold ISOs will do for you. I'll guarantee you, they'll make you feel better than you've ever felt in your life, plus I believe they're the quickest way to rehabilitate any injury of any kind, because they flush the muscle or joint or tendon and ligament with blood and oxygen without movement.

Another good example of what the benefits of ISOs are is, say, for football players: How many times have you seen a football player's side knee blow out from a hit or a speed cut sideways with the leg when he's running. With ISOs you can build this side knee strength up. With regular weights it is very hard to do.

For building side knee strength with isometrics, take a piece of wood, say, a two-foot long piece of 2 x 12, put steel brackets on each end of the board, and drill holes in a concrete floor. Make the bottom of the steel brackets solid steel rod and drill the holes just deep enough and make the rod just high enough so that the 2 x 12 piece of wood is above your ankle but below your knee height from the ground. Now what you do is put a brace plate along the outside of where your foot would be. If you put your side knee up alongside the 2 x 12 so now your foot is wedged in and your knee is pushing sideways against the 2 x 12, you can lean slightly sideways and in this position can apply great pressure to your side knee. This builds your side knee tendons up to great strength levels.

I believe what causes a lot of injuries is complete underdevelopment of the little muscles. If all you do is work the big muscles but don't spend time on the little controller muscles, this is what causes all kinds of injuries in all kinds of sports. And throwing ISOs in your routine can cure this problem because you can work so many different muscle angles so quickly and tirelessly. I have read thousands of magazines, and nobody ever talks about building the little muscles and tying them all in with the big for superior coordination, except maybe in karate magazines.

Bruce Lee knew what speed strength was. And I found out with my hay hauling, and now I have brought it to light for you, the reader. If you decide to try these sometime, they will give you a form of strength that chances are you've never experienced before.

CHAPTER 5

Running with Weight

Running with weight builds tremendous explosive power and super strong toes, feet, ankles, knees, and hips, back—the whole body. But the most stress hits the ankles. If you have weak ankles, running with a solid barbell behind your neck on your shoulders will expose a weak pair of ankles, knees, and groin in a hurry. Running with weight, either a barbell behind the shoulders, dumbbells or kettlebells in hands, or a sandbag on one or both shoulders, is a great exercise to build strength in areas that no other lift can build. Imagine the power your body would possess if you could work up to running with 500 lb. on your shoulders for a block or two.

I believe the strongest feet and ankles in the world belong to the sumo wrestlers of Japan. The true masters of karate also possess strong ankles, and gymnasts also have superior ankle strength. I submit that any body movement, forward, backward, and sideways, starts from foot and ankle strength. If you want to be powerful in body movements such as running, pushing, pulling, or on the wrestling mat, you must have or develop superior foot and ankle, knee and groin strength. The sumo wrestler is continually building his ankle strength in his pushing and pulling movements. Running with weight will give you great explosive power also.

Running with weight should be done at a half sprint, because if you practice at a full sprint, the price you could pay for just a split-second lack of concentration or foot slip could be devastating. When you run with weight, the G-forces generated are tremendous. I believe in a sprint that is three-quarters the power of your full sprint. The G-force raises your foot impact weight anywhere from 7 to 10 G's.

Let's say a world-class sprinter who weighs 200 lb. sprints 100 yards in nine seconds. Now every time his foot hits the ground, that is 10 G's x 200 lb.; that translates into 2000 lb. per foot in a sprinter of that weight at that speed. When you run with weight, you can get the same intensity without having to generate the dangerous speed.

Say for instance you're a 200-lb. lifter, and you do a half sprint with 100 lb. on your back; at a half sprint, you're probably generating three to four G's. When we figure this out, a 200-lb. lifter with 100 lb. on his back, or 300 lb. total x 4 G's equals 1200 lb. of G-force every step.,

After a couple of months you're running with 200 lb. on your back. Now the equation is 200 lb. plus 200 lb., or 400 lb. total x 4 G's, which equals 1600 lb. of G-force every step. After another couple of months, you're up to 300 lb. on your back. Now the equation is 500 lb. x 4 G's, which equals 2000 lb. of G-force: After just four months of training, you're creating the same G-force on your legs that a world-class sprinter generates.

Now you can carry the same force as a world-class sprinter in your legs. If you then threw the weights down and started out slowly sprinting for speed, how long do you think it would be before you would be a world-class sprinter yourself. I submit to you, in my opinion, not very long, because you are supporting the same load as the sprinter and the basic strength is there. All you have to do is to do it faster. It is just like both of you, above, doing the same amount of work output (generating the same G-force) in the same distance. Now that you can do the same amount of work, all you have to do is stretch out and slowly practice pulling the fast twitch muscles into play, by practicing sprinting and by toning with the use of isometrics.

But a lot of you will never wish to run fast, so you'll just keep increasing the weight you run with on your shoulders to keep building your tremendous strength up to even higher levels. Football players would find this exercise very useful for their game, as would wrestlers, sprinters, gymnasts, hockey players, soccer players—practically anybody in sports.

The way I developed this philosophy was through a buddy of mine. He's been doing wrist curls since he was a kid, and he got to where he did 285 for 10 to 15 reps with a revolving Olympic bar. He worked up to where he could hold 500 for a negative hold just slightly beyond his knees. In other words, he had tremendous wrist strength. But what I'm getting at, and here's the point, is that he loved to barroom brawl, and he's been all around the country just for that purpose. And seldom would his fights last over one or two punches.

Now he had slightly above average upper body strength—I think he benched 275—but I was stronger in every area of my body than he was and could tie him in a 40-yard sprint. But his wrist-curling strength was twice what mine is. He and I were talking about it, and he told me the reason he could knock out everybody was his wrist strength built by the wrist curl.

One day we were at a friend's house and he had a full-size heavy punching bag hanging in the basement. We put on some light gloves and were having a contest to see who could punch it the farthest, to see how high it would swing. Well, I gave it everything I had and darn near broke my wrist. Then my buddy tried it, and he knocked that bag higher than I did. Right there I had learned a lesson. If you want to deliver tremendous body power through the arm, you have to have a powerful wrist.

The same holds true for the ankle when it comes to tremendous power in propelling the body. If you really want to get powerful in the weight run, I would recommend starting with a weight that feels really light and doing 10 sets of 30 to 50 step sprints every day, working up in weight whenever you feel ready. This exercise also gives you super strength in the groin area and knee joint. If you're concentrating on other exercises also, I'd throw it in once or twice a week. Oh, another thing to watch out for when you're first starting out in this movement is loose gravel, rocks, or uneven ground. Eventually you can handle running on all these when you get strong enough, but when first starting out, I'd be careful.

Now what I do is I set up two racks or two sets of squat stands outdoors, and run from one set to the other. But if you've only got one, just run out, stop, turn around, and run back. Or if you use sand bags or rubber truck inner tube with sand, you can just throw it down at the end of your run. Or you can just jerk a barbell from ground over your head, put behind your neck, and run, and then press it up and set it down each time. Use your imagination and improvise with whatever you've got to work with.

CHAPTER 6

Singles Build Tremendous Strength

The old time lifters did a lot of singles training in their time, and some of the records they set back in the 1960s are still unbroken, so the power of doing singles for gaining strength is tremendous if utilized in the right way. I myself have made great and speedy gains from singles, so here are some strategies for you to make singles work.

Singles Workout Strategy No. 1—One Lift
When working one lift with singles, for example one lift you would like to practice and excel in and maybe set a world record in, here is a routine that is very efficient and will build tremendous strength:

#1. Lift every day, seven days a week.

#2. Use 70% of your maximum effort in your lift when starting out, and as you gain strength, keep using weights that are at 70% of your max.

#3. During **Week 1**:

- Day 1—Do three singles the first day with one to two minutes' rest between each single.
- Day 2—Do five singles with the same weight as Day I, with one to two minutes' rest between each one.
- Day 3—Do seven singles with the same weight as Day 1, with one to two minutes' rest between each one.
- Day 4—Do nine singles with the same weight as Day 1, with the same amount of rest between each one as above.
- Day 5—Do 11 singles with the same weight as Day 1, with the same rest.

- Day 6—Do 13 singles with the same weight as Day 1, with the same rest.
- Day 7—Do 15 singles with the same weight as Day 1, with the same rest—a minute or two between each set.

You have now made a complete cycle and are at **Week 2**, Day 1. Now you will add five or 10 pounds and go through the whole cycle again.

#4. Once a month, test your max to make sure you are using weights in your weekly cycle that are 70% of your max. If your weekly cycle weight for that week was under 70% of your max, add weight to your routine to adjust. If your weekly cycle weight was more than 70% of your max, take weight off and adjust. This monthly testing of your max will keep you in the target zone.

This workout must be done seven days a week, 365 days a year. Each week, you are building your endurance and toughening your tendons and ligaments by doing more work toward the end of each cycle, and then during the next week, or cycle as I call it, you're adding more weight and doing it all over again. The great thing about this type of training is that you will build great strength without really ever making yourself tired because the body is adjusting naturally and rhythmically.

Singles Workout Strategy No. 2—One Lift
Again, when working on just one lift:

#1. Lift every other day, seven days a week, 365 days a year.

#2. Use weights that are 70% of your max.

#3. Do 30 singles with between one to two minutes' rest between each single. When you reach a total of 30, you are done. Rest a day. Then add five pounds the next workout and do 30 singles, with one to two minutes' rest between each single. Rest a day. Add five pounds every other day, resting one day in between, and so on and so forth.

#4. Then once every two weeks, max out and adjust your weekly poundage to make sure you are using 70% of your max. If you're using under 70%, add weight to adjust. If you're using over 70%, take weight off to adjust. This will keep you in the target zone.

Singles Workout Strategy No. 3—Three Lifts

When you are working on three lifts as in powerlifting; for example, the bench, squat, and deadlift:

#1. Lift every day, seven days a week, 365 days a year.

#2. Do four singles in each lift with one to two minutes' rest between each single, and go from one lift to next quickly. Start with the squat, then go to the bench, then go to the deadlift; use 70% of your max.

#3. Add five pounds to your bench every three days; add ten pounds to your squat and deadlift every four days.

#4. Max out every three weeks in all three lifts. If using weights in excess of 70%, reduce weight to adjust. If using weights under 70%, add weight to adjust. This will keep you in your target zone. Concentrate on speed when performing the lifts during your daily workouts.

Singles Workout Strategy No. 4—Three Lifts

When training three lifts, as in powerlifting (e.g. squat, bench and deadlift):

#1. Train every other day, seven days a week, 365 days a year.

#2. Train bench squat, bench deadlift, bench squat, bench deadlift, every other day, so on and so forth.

#3. Do 25 singles with a minute to two minutes' rest between each single in the deadlift and the squat, and do 12 singles in the bench on each squat and deadlift day. For example:

Mon—squat 25 singles, bench 12 singles
Tues—off
Wed—deadlift 25 singles, bench 12 singles
Thurs—off
Fri—squat 25 singles, bench 12 singles
Sat—off
Sun—deadlift 25 singles, bench 12 singles

#4. Every week add twenty pounds to your squat and deadlift and ten pounds to your bench.

#5. Every month, max out in each lift and if the poundages you're using in your weekly workouts are over 70%, adjust and decrease your weight to match. If the weight is under 70% of your max, add weight to your weekly workouts and adjust. This way you stay at your target weight of 70% max in workouts.

Singles Workout Strategy No. 5—Ten or More Lifts
When you are working on 10-15 different lifts:
#1. Work *two days on, one off*, seven days a week, 365 days a year. Work all 10-15 lifts on each day.
#2. Do two singles in each lift with one to two minutes' rest between each lift, and for each single, use weights at 70% max.
#3. Add five to ten pounds to each lift every three days.
#4. Every two weeks max out in every lift; adjust all weights in your daily workouts to 70% of your max in each lift. The day that you max will be your workout for that day.

Singles Workout Strategy No. 6—Thirty or More Lifts
When working 30-40 different lifts:
#1. Work every other day or once every three days, depending on how you feel. Do all 30-40 lifts in one workout.
#2. Do one single in each lift, moving from one lift to the next every two to three minutes. Use 70% of max to 85% of max.
#3. Add five to ten pounds to each lift once a week.
#4. Max out on all lifts once a month; then adjust all lifts to fit between 70% to 85% of your max on each lift. This will keep you in your target zone.

The Target Zone
This is what I call the target zone: It is a percentage of your maximum effort in any lift, and to me the target zone should be between 70% to 80% of your maximum effort in any one lift. This is the zone you must stay in when training to get stronger the fastest. I believe the 70% of max range is better than the 80% of max range.

There cannot be enough said about staying in this zone to develop super strength. With me, even after 15 years of training, I still catch myself trying to jump out of the zone and constantly have to monitor my ambition of wanting to lift too heavy too fast. Nothing will stop your progress in your quest for strength faster

Steve Justa in the start position of the quarter deadlift, or hand and thigh lift.

than when you try to lift too heavy too fast. There are a lot of factors involved here that must be dealt with and I will do that for you. I just cannot stress how important this is. The target zone is something to learn, and learn well.

There are two important things to remember about the target zone:

#1. *When you exceed the target zone, that is when you go too heavy in your lifting too fast.* When you go past 70% of your max, something happens to you mentally.

Let's say your max is 500 in the deadlift, and you've worked up to the point where you're pulling 450 for reps, say three reps, and you want to do four sets of three reps for your workout. Well, this is fine for one workout. Even if you're tough mentally, as you start lifting and gut your way through the workout, because you're lifting so close to your max, every rep is hard and every set is hard. If you make it through this workout, when you finally make it, you say to yourself, "I'm on the verge of lifting too heavy, but I made it and I feel happy, but it will feel lighter next workout—it has to because I don't know how many more workouts like that last one I can endure."

It's at this point your mind's already giving out on you because you're questioning yourself if you could work that hard again if you had to. Then, until your next workout, this feeling of dread sticks with you, and if you're going to use the same weight this time as last, you know you're in for trouble. You know you're out of your target zone but you want to push ahead rather than have to take weight off and start all over again.

For some reason, to the ambitious strength athlete, the thought of having to take weight off of a lift you've already done is a fate worse than death itself. And this is a mentality you must not carry. Never ever be ashamed or embarrassed or feel let down because you have to take a little weight off a lift to keep training. If it feels too heavy to you, it probably *is* too heavy for you to be training with.

But getting back to the story, you approach your next workout with dread because you know it's going to be a killer mentally and physically, but you're expecting it to be a little lighter than last time since you've already had one workout with this weight. So you hit the workout and for some reason it feels even heavier to you this time than it did last time. Well, now you've really got trouble mentally when this happens, and you really feel frustrated. But no, you think, I'm tough, I can handle it. So you gut your way through another backbreaking workout, carrying a sense of dread and de-struction with you the whole time—when all you had to do was take off 100 lb. and go through a rewarding, happy, carefree work-out with plenty of confidence.

This is why I say you must stay within your target zone. I preach about this all through my book about staying within your limits; it is the single biggest factor in defeat when talking super strength. The two biggest factors in successfully developing super strength are staying in your target zone while training, and training with rhythm and consistency. No matter what routine you do, your body will adapt as long as you don't completely overwork yourself or get out of your target zone.

#2. *The second thing about the target zone that makes it work is the speed factor.* When you pull or push a weight with speed or quickness, you will gain strength ten times faster than if you're lifting heavy maximum weight slowly; and if you go too light, it just isn't heavy enough to be really effective quickly. Compare it to kicking a ball. For example, if you kicked a heavy medicine ball, how far would it go? Now, if you kicked a balloon, how far would it go? Finally, if you kicked a basketball, how far would it go? It would go the farthest the most efficiently, and creates almost the perfect transference of a power curve.

The same is true in weightlifting. If you haven't got the right medium to transfer your power into, you'll have a hard time building power. If it's too heavy, it's too hard; if it's too light, it's too light. What could be simpler? I would say anything between 60% to 70% max is the perfect power range, curve, or target zone to stay in—however you want to say it. So the weights in the percentage zone will give you the perfect medium to apply your power to transfer your energy so you can develop your horsepower. It is so simple, yet so hard to really do. You must put that ego aside and really get down to business. Good luck.

CHAPTER 7

The Hand and Thigh Lift or the Quarter Deadlift

The hand and thigh lift, along with the backlift, is the ultimate test for upper leg and hip strength. The whole subject of super strength can be covered with the practice of the hand and thigh lift, but first let's talk about just what exactly it is. The hand and thigh lift is when you have a bar at mid-thigh height and you pull the weight with your hands and thighs up off the ground. The object of the lift is to break the weight off the ground an inch or two with the force of your legs pushing up against the bar, and your hands are gripping the bar pulling up also.

Now, there are several ways of setting this lift up. One way is to use a barbell off blocks so the bar is at a height where you can bend your knees under the bar and the bar rests on your upper thigh. You have to have the bar high enough to be able to get your upper thighs under the bar when your knees are bent; then you use the force of your legs pressing up against the bar to help you lift the bar.

The barbell placed in the power rack will work also. Place the barbell on top of the pins in the power rack at the right height so that when you lift the bar and your legs are straight, the bar will be only a few inches above the pins. Using this style, you must use the reverse grip to keep the bar from spinning out of your hands. The reverse grip is one hand with the palm facing your body and the other hand with the palm facing away from your body.

If you use blocks to lift the barbell from, you should make the blocks just high enough so that after you have lifted the weight, the bottom of the plates are just a few inches higher than the blocks. I would recommend wrapping the bar with foam or a towel, or wear two pairs of tight-fitting blue jeans with an unwrapped or padded bar. This will keep the bar from ripping the skin off your legs when you get to where you're using a lot of weight.

Another method for bar setup is to use a bar with a cable clamped around the middle of the bar; the bar and your hands rest on your front thighs, with a pad of some sort on your thighs, and the cable runs down between your legs and is hooked to weights that you straddle with your legs. Or you are up on a platform built above the weight, and you run the cable down through the platform and hook it to the weight below. Now in using this style, you do not have to use the reverse grip because if you have your cable bolted to your bar or have it running through a hole in your bar and clamped, the weight hanging down below your bar will keep your bar from spinning out of your hands.

The third setup is to have the bar running through and bolted to steel barrels. Thirty- or fifty-gallon oil barrels work well. For this, you weld little plates of steel down from your bar, drill holes in them and bolt them to your steel barrels. Put one barrel on each side and you stand to lift in between them. Lift with your hands outside the legs and lift with the legs under bar; there is no need to use the reverse grip in this style either. In this style, I would use a solid steel, cold rolled bar about 1-1/2 inches in diameter, and seven to eight feet long. In the style of the cable between the legs, I would use a smaller diameter bar, maybe a 1-1/4 or a 1-inch bar.

Now that you have a basic idea of the lift and the setup, I will tell you what the lift will do for you and how to approach the mechanics of the lift. Steady practice of the hand and thigh lift will give your body a strength that no other lift can match, because the hand and thigh works your body from head to toe. After working the lift, you will feel a certain kind of rush of stoutness from head to toe. You will feel a solid tie-in of all your major muscles—your traps, shoulders, biceps, forearm, hands, triceps, back, sides, hips, legs, calves, feet. This lift allows maximum power to be generated through the legs and hips, which shoots right up through the rest of your upper body.

The hand and thigh lift also will build crushing strength in your hands and will build tremendous back-pressure pulling power with your fingers and hand. This lift will build superstrong trapezius muscles, along with hip, leg, and back muscles, and strong forearms and back. If you've never done the lift before and you start, it will give you a real feeling of total body power. The hand and thigh lift will give you a satisfaction of a strength tie-in through your whole body. It is the only lift that I can say I've ever done

Steve Justa doing a one-ton deadlift lockout with a 10-second hold.

that, after I have practiced it thoroughly, it gives my mind and my body a satisfaction that I have worked all my muscles plenty for that day.

Great poundages are possible in this lift with practice. I have pulled over 2000 lb. in this lift on many an occasion. I have torn quarter-sized chunks of skin right out of my palms many a time also on this lift. I wrap the bar with cloth athletic tape and then rub chalk into the tape for added pulling power with the palms and fingers. A good tip to avoid pulling chunks of skin out of the palms of your hand when you start using really heavy weight is this:

When your hands and fingers start to feel a stinging stiffness on the surface of the skin, stop lifting immediately because these are the signals that precede a palm tear or finger tear.

Say, for example, you have done 20 or 30 total reps already in your workout and on your next rep or set, the skin on your palms or fingers starts to generate a stinging and cramping type of feeling. You had better stop your workout for the day because if you don't, on the very next rep your palm could tear right open and when this happens you won't be able to practice the lift again for two weeks—that's how long it takes to heal a bad palm tear. It's happened to me a lot, and I know better, too, but I thought, ah, what the heck, just one more rep—and that one more rep is what got me. Then it throws your momentum and your whole routine out of whack.

When your hand finally does heal up, you've got to drop weight and try to toughen your skin up again, because after a two-week layoff, your skin has lost its toughness and you can have the whole thing happen again, more easily this time. Then you've lost a whole month of training. I have gone from pulling 2000 lb. one minute to not being able to lift an empty bar in about two seconds with a bad palm tear, especially when using a 1-1/2-inch diameter bar, because at least half or more of the pressure to pull with comes from the palm of the hand.

The hand and thigh is a true test of toughness, mentally and physically. The mechanics of the lift parallel the skills also used in the backlift. When you go to lift great weight off the ground, you must coordinate every muscle into action in a split second with great explosion. No matter how strong you are, you will not lift a huge weight from the ground unless you have great concentration and coordination and explosion. Practice makes perfect; the more you practice, the better you will become at this.

And never push through after your initial blast of power fails to move the weight. If your initial blast doesn't move the weight, say on your sixth rep, and you go for seven reps and you blast your power into the seventh rep and it moves a little or doesn't move, stop, because if you try to push through and grind the rep out, you're asking for serious trouble in the form of an injury. Either stop and rest three or four minutes and then do some more reps, or drop 200 pounds or call it good for the day and wait till the next workout. When handling weights of over one-half ton or in the tons, you mustn't push through or grind reps because you're asking for serious injury.

In the hand and thigh lift, secure yourself under bar, relax totally, then, in a split second, push up with legs, pull with your hands, and coordinate and blast the power; and if you're trying to max out, if you don't move the weight fast right away, stop instantly because if you don't you're asking for trouble.

When training the hand and thigh lift, what worked best for me was using singles to practice the lift. If you look at Chapter 6 on singles training, you can choose from two or three singles programs the one you would like to use.   I would recommend Singles Strategy No. 1 exclusively for the hand and thigh lift.

The reason I use singles in this lift is because reps will tire you out so fast when you start piling the weight on. For me with singles, I can create more intensity without getting too tired too quickly, so that's what I would suggest. Plus, your hands won't tear so easily.

So give it all you've got and good luck.

CHAPTER 8

The Back Lift

A back lift is where you lift a wooden or steel platform or table off the ground an inch or two. I believe the back lift is the supreme test of overall body strength; it is the position in which the human body can lift the most weight. Two of the greatest strongmen that ever lived, Louis Cyr and Paul Anderson, were excellent back lifters. Paul Anderson owns the world record at 6270 lb. Louis Cyr used to lift 4400 lb. on a regular basis and has done an unofficial 5000-lb. lift in practice. Now, until you've ever climbed under a two-ton platform and tried to lift this weight, the average man has no appreciation of how heavy and how hard this weight is to move. But with the right training, the two-ton lift is possible for anybody who wants to pay his dues.

The back lift builds tremendous tendon and ligament strength. The technical aspects are, first of all, centering your body under the weight. If you're off-center over a couple of inches any direction, the lift won't leave its resting place level. So you'll just have to move around underneath and lift, testing different positions until you get it right. When you do, you'll know it.

Another tip is to center your body so your legs will be lifting over two-thirds of the weight and your arms the remainder, so you'll want your legs under the center of the platform and arms on the outside edge. Another thing is, sometimes even when you are centered at the right spot and one side of the lift comes up and the other side doesn't, you may be pushing slightly harder with one leg than the other. Concentrate on making totally coordinated movements, evenly pushing with both legs and arms.

If you're 6'2" tall, the distance from the bottom of the platform to the ground level would approximately be 42" to 46", depending on how heavy your bodyweight is. You place your whole back up against the bottom of your table or platform. Your whole upper body will be under the platform with your whole upper body parallel to the ground. Your legs will be straight up and down, in a vertical position. And your knees will be slightly bent as your back rests under the table; your legs should also be slightly wider than your shoulders, and your arms should be vertical to the ground and the palms of your hands resting on a low stool or block with your elbows slightly bent. Then the object of the lift is to push up and straighten your arms and legs and lift the platform off of its supports, or lift the table off the ground, an inch or two.

Now, at the start of the lift, you must summon all your strength and explode in a totally coordinated blast of power that is all done in a split second. Momentum plays a big part in this lift and that comes from concentrating through the lift. For example, let's say you wanted to punch a board with your fist and break it. To do that, you imagine your fist going through the board to behind the board. The same principle holds true for the back lift. With practice you will develop this skill—a total blast and concentration of power, speed, and strength, all combined in a split second.

Building a Back Lift

An easy and cheap way to build a back lift is to go out and buy three railroad ties. Then, go to a steel yard and buy four 4-foot long, heavy angle irons at least 1/4-inch thick, and drill one 1/2-inch hole at each end of each angle iron. Get four long bolts and nuts so you can put two angle irons on each end of the ties. Put your railroad ties together, flat side by side, and put two angle irons on each end of the ties, top and bottom, and bolt them together on each end.

Now go out and get four 55-gallon empty steel drums. Figure out the right height for the drums to sit off the ground, and put two drums on one side and two drums on the other side so that your railroad ties will sit across the top of the drums with room enough for you to get underneath. Then get a straight long stick or board and lay it across the barrels; this will give you an idea of how high you'll have to raise your barrels off of the ground so when your back is under the board, your knees should be slightly bent. You can use boards, bricks, plywood, or dirt inside a wood frame to raise your barrels to the right height.

Once you get the right height figured out, get your barrels set and fill them half full of dirt, gravel, or sand; this will give you a really sturdy, safe and steady base to lift your platform of railroad

A back lift loaded and ready to rumble.

ties off of. Put your railroad ties up on the barrels and get yourself a low stool or block or something like that to put your hands on. This should be about shoulder-width. I would also nail 2 x 4's about two feet or three feet tall vertically all around your back lift to hold the weight on. For weight, you could use rocks, concrete bags, bags of sand, or put a plastic tarp over the top inside of your back lift and scoop dirt or sand in. Or you can go to the junkyard and buy used steel in short pieces. These usually sell for 80 dollars a ton.

This is the cheapest way to build a back lift. If you have the money, you could go to a blacksmith's shop and have a steel table built for yourself, preferably one that assembles and disassembles, with heavy bolts, but this would be very expensive. And now you're ready to start back lifting.

A concrete floor, preferably rough concrete, is the best surface to back lift on. If you have smooth concrete, make sure there's no dirt or oil that will cause your feet to slip. Another tip is to get a pair of lace-up boots with very low heels that fit very tightly. This back lifting will put extreme stress on your feet and ankles, especially when you get up to the 3000-lb. range and over. I personally use tight-fitting, low-cut, leather dress shoes that I purposely tore the heels off of so that my feet are flat on the floor. I can generate the most power using this kind of shoe, and it also gives me great ankle support because my foot is close to the floor.

Performing the Back Lift

To train for the back lift, I would start out with a weight that feels light, and for the first week I would do sets of 10 to 20 reps. Keep counting the reps and add them up after each set, and when you get 100 total reps, stop. I would do this every other day for the first week to break your muscles in, then the second week add 100 lb. to your break-in weight. Now the second week, do 70 total reps; do 7 sets of 10 reps until your total is 70 reps, then stop, and do this workout every other day for three or four days your second week. Then *add* 10 lb. to the lift every week and continue your three to four days a week of every other day, 7 sets of 10 reps. If you get to where the weight gets so heavy that you can't get seven sets of 10 reps, you punish yourself and stay at the same weight until you can. Then go back to adding 10 lb. a week again and continue.

Another thing you'll have to learn is when you back lift, the lift will a lot of times move out of position while you lift it and sometimes you'll have to constantly slightly readjust your position in between reps. The more you practice, the better you will get at this. Sometimes you'll be in a perfect lifting groove and won't have to readjust once—you'll do 10 reps without readjusting; but other times you'll have to readjust three or four times in 10 reps.

Steve Justa repping out in the back lift with 3800 to 4000 lb. Angle irons are between six and seven feet long.

But come to expect this, and if the lift gets angled off-center, you'll have to learn to readjust it inch by inch as you rep out with it; or lift it up and hold it and force it to spin with a slight twist of the back until it's in the right position, then lower.

Sometimes your lift will have a tendency to work itself forward. An easy way to correct this is when it gets too far to one side of the barrels, you move your hand stool or block to the other side and reverse your position and the lift will automatically work back to the other side. So keep this in mind and come to expect it.

Another way to back lift is to lift and hold for time. If you choose this way, I would use the one-minute hold. So pick a weight you can lift and hold for one minute. Once you get the minute hold, the next workout *add* 50 lb. and once you can do one minute again, *add* 50 lb. again. I would do one hold per day and do this every day, seven days a week. I wouldn't mix the hold with the reps systems because it seems to be counterproductive. I would do either one or the other; either way works well and will get you the same development in the end. I will say that the hold lifting in the back lift is extremely tough on your feet.

I hope my tips will prove useful. Good luck.

CHAPTER 9

Partial Movements

Partial movements are vital training assets for anyone's lifting regimen. Partials are movements such as:

- breaking a barbell a couple of inches off the floor;
- the quarter squat;
- the bench press lockout, where you put the barbell in a power rack and set it at a height to where you just have to lift the weight up a couple of inches and your arms are fully extended, holding the barbell in a locked-out position;
- the quarter deadlift in the power rack or in the standing position;
- lifting the barbell in the military press position, or just lifting it off the rack and holding it at neck level;
- lifting a big, heavy rock off a stand and just holding it, or lifting a heavy rock off a slightly higher stand and holding it at chest height;
- doing high box squats, squatting down on a box about 27 inches high;
- doing backlifts;
- lifting a heavy bar up a few inches off a power rack with one shoulder
- lifting a barbell off a power rack about knee height, with arms bent, and standing erect with arms bent with the bar in your hands, palms up, holding the bar at your waist with arms still bent at right angles.

Or any other partial movement you can think of.

The great thing about partial movements is they build great tendon strength and toughen your body for full range movements. In partial movements you can use a lot more weight than you can in full range movements because you're not moving the weight as far as in a full range movement. And the overload of the heavier weight toughens your muscles and tendons and ligaments and bones into the heavier weight. Also, great amounts of blood can be pumped throughout your body to totally saturate your muscles, without your becoming too fatigued, especially if you do 10 to 15 quick sets of 5 reps each set. In this fashion, you're building powerful tendon strength and ligament strength; you're generating maximum muscle saturation of oxygen and blood.

All this makes you a lot stronger in your full range movements a lot quicker because with the partial movements, you're working the big muscles and most powerful ones, the ones closest to your joints. It is hard to work these muscles and tendons thoroughly enough with full range lifts. So it is to your total benefit to mix partial range movements in with your full range movements. You will, in that way, be working your body much more thoroughly and also will gain tremendous confidence in your full range movements.

An added benefit is that partial movements toughen you so as to keep you from injuries in your full range movements. I would compare it to the power of a horse's hindquarters. The main blast of power of a horse comes from high up at the joint at the hips and lower back. To get really good at the art of super strength, I believe you must work the muscles super hard and intensely high up at the joints, like the driving power of that race horse's hindquarters have. The hind legs higher up don't move very far but they generate tremendous power in a short movement.

I believe the human body is the same in this sense. And to develop super strength in the shortest time, you should not exclude partial movements from your workout. You must work the muscles intensely from top to bottom and bottom to top.

One of the strongest men who ever lived, Paul Anderson, always mixed partial movements in with full range movements in practically every lift he ever did. And Paul made tremendous gains of strength at a tremendous rate of time. My philosophy is that of Anderson: If you're going to lift weights, you might as well work the muscles thoroughly because it will pay off for you quickly. Most of the greatest strongmen of history included some sort of partial movements in their training.

Partial movements build tremendous strength. For example, if I wanted to become a world-record holder in the deadlift, what I would do is one of two routines:

Routine No. 1
Day #I—Put a weight on the bar that you can lift two inches off the ground for 5 reps, then rest 30 seconds to a minute; do another set, then rest again, and do this until you've done 10 to 15 sets of 5 reps. You must use a weight light enough so that you can get 10 to 15 sets of 5 reps in a half-hour or less. If you can't get the work done in this time frame, you're going too heavy too quickly. Now this is Day #1.

Day #2—Go to quarter deadlifts in the power rack or off blocks; put the bar at a height about three inches above the knee or just high enough so your thighs will fit under the bar with your legs slightly bent. Pick the bar up to mid-thigh, standing erectly with the weight, and do the same sets and reps as you did for Day #1's workout, that is, 10 to 15 sets of 5 reps in 30 minutes or less. When you have done this, you're now done with Day #2.

Day #3—Go to the full range deadlift. Use a weight about 60% of your maximum pull and do 6 to 7 single reps, concentrating on speed; rest about 20 seconds in between each rep. Pull these reps fast when executing them with about 60% of your max; concentrate on each pull thoroughly, and pull with 80% of your top speed in each single rep.

Now rest for about five minutes after the 6 to 7 single reps and work up to a weight you can't pull, making 50-pound jumps, as follows: Take the weight you had on the bar that you were pulling for speed, which was 60% of your max, and *add* 50 pounds and lift it. Then rest a minute and a half, and *add* 50 pounds more and lift it; then rest again, and *add* 50 pounds more, and so on until you can't pull it to your waist. When you reach the weight you can't pull, you are then done with your workout for Day #3.

Take a day off and let your body rest, and then start all over again with Day #1's workout; the next day, Day #2's workout; the next day, Day #3's workout; then take another day off, letting the body rest, and then start all over again.

Now the key to the whole routine is Day #3, which is the full range deadlift. You will use this as your gauge when to *add* weight to your Day #1 and Day #2 workouts. You should remember the weight on the bar at the end of Day #3's workout that stopped you, that is, your first Day #3 workout weight that stopped you when you were *adding* 50 pounds each jump.

Steve Justa lifting over 1000 lb. off the rack on one shoulder.

Let's say, for example, you pulled 500 lb., then you *added* your 50 lbs. and tried 550. Well, 550 stopped you and you couldn't pull it, so 12 days later you work up to your 550 again at the end of Day #3's workout, but this time you pull it. So now you take your day off, and then the next day for Day #1's workout you will *add* 50 pounds to the weight you've been breaking off the floor a couple of inches; and then the next day, for Day #2's workout, you will *add* 100 pounds to your quarter deadlift weight and use that much weight for Day #2 in your quarter deadlift.

When you can pull another extra 50 pounds in your full range deadlift on Day #3, which would be 600 lb., when your next Day #1 comes up, *add* another 50 pounds to your break-off-the-floor lift, and the next day *add* another 100 pounds to your quarter deadlift weight. Continue to *add* your weight in this manner. You may have to keep rereading what I have told you to remember and grasp it. This is a simple yet complicated concept.

Routine No. 2

The other routine I would use, if you don't like the one on the three-day cycle and rest a day, is this: I would do *all* three movements every day, seven days a week—the two-inch deadlift off the floor, the quarter deadlift, and the full range deadlift, all three during the same workout, day in and day out.

And I would do them in this manner:

First, use a weight about 85% of your maximum pull in the two-inch deadlift break, and do 3 sets of 2 reps with 30 seconds' rest between sets.

Rest two minutes.

Go to your quarter deadlift and use a weight 70% of your max, and do 3 sets of 7 to 10 reps with two minutes' rest in between each set.

Go to the full range deadlift and start with a weight 60% of your max, and do three singles for speed with 10 seconds' rest in between each single.

Then go in 50-pound jumps to a higher weight and do a single pull at each 50-pound jump until you get to a weight you can't pull. Rest a minute between these 50-pound jump pulls, *adding* 50 pounds each successive pull, and go until you fail to pull the weight, then quit.

Go through the same thing the next day, day after day, seven days a week. And when you finally pull that 50-pound jump in the full range deadlift that you couldn't the day before, the next day *add* 50 pounds to your two-inch break-off-the-floor lift and *add* 100 to the quarter deadlift. Continue *adding* weight in this manner. In this routine you're constantly testing your maximum pull, day after day.

These two philosophies or strategies can be used in any lift where safety racks can be used to catch the weight if you fail to push or pull, or where you don't need safety racks. In lifts like the clean and jerk, you must not go in 50-pound jumps to failure because you would end up killing yourself. So basically follow the same principles, except stop before you get to your maximum and just stay with a medium-heavy weight until that weight feels lighter, and when it noticeably feels lighter to you, *add* 10 to 20 lb. the next day your workout calls for you to do it. These are two workouts to use when concentrating on maximum gains in minimum time on one lift.

When incorporating partial movements into a routine with a lot of other lifts, just throw in a set of partials here and there on a fairly consistent basis and you can't go wrong. And do enough reps or sets in the partials to get a pump feeling going in your muscles, then call it good.

Now, partial movements for the clean and jerk involve about six to seven different partial movements, because the clean and jerk is such a complicated lift that moves the weight a long distance. All partial movements will help all lifts, but in lifts like the clean and jerk, I would recommend the following:

- the standing jerk picked off a power rack or the partial jerk from chest to top of head;
- overhead lockouts to arm's length, from elbows slightly bent to lockout overhead in the power rack;
- two-inch deadlift breaks off floor;
- six-inch pulls for speed from below the knee to above the knee
- mid-thigh hang pulls to the lower chest for speed, as well as chest to overhead jerks
- using a power rack in the squat position, do slight bounces in a rock-bottom position, holding the bar at the chest with your hands
- seated and standing partial good mornings using a power rack
- partial box squats with the bar behind neck, to about 27 inches high
- bent arm lift off rack and hold palms down from mid-thigh to waist for 15 seconds.

These are the partial movements to use to help clean and jerk. There are a lot of full range movements also, but that is not what this chapter is about.

The Russians, who have produced some of the strongest Olympic lifters in history, do all kinds of partial movements in their workouts, which I believe is responsible for the tremendous poundage they move in these lifts. The Russians do a lot of two to three reps for six sets with around 80 to 85% max in their partials and full movements. I would do partials with the bar across one shoulder in a power rack, with a pad on the shoulder, for stomach and midsection stability and side leg and hip strength. When doing partials, you can use reps, or lift the weight and hold it for time; both build strength. The hand and thigh lift or quarter deadlift, the backlift, the quarter squat in the power rack, and the push press are my favorite partial movements. Also shoulder lifting, with the bar across the top of the shoulder, with a pad on the shoulder; the deadlift off the ground a few inches; and the deadlift just above the knee are others that I like.

When I discovered how valuable partials are, I learned that they also help you have a lot fewer injuries or, in other words, they will help keep you injury-free. You toughen the body without having to move the weight very far, if you're careful not to go too heavy too fast.

CHAPTER 10

The Shovel or Pitchfork Lift

I haven't been training on this lift personally for very long, maybe three months or so. But already the strength this lift has given me has helped me in virtually every other lift. What is the most difficult type of weight to lift? An awkward weight, or any weight that is away or far away from the spinal column, because it puts maximum stress on the muscles from severe angles.

Let me give you an idea why I call it the shovel lift or the pitchfork lift. The reason I call it this is because it mimics the motion of using a shovel or a pitchfork—which I'm sure at one time or another all of you have done. And also it copies the motion of grabbing one end of a long tree branch or limb and lifting it off the ground, and I bet you've all done this at one time or another. This will give you a small idea of what kind of stress this can produce on the body.

Now let's imagine you have a heavy pipe or steel shaft about five feet long with a flat steel plate welded to one end. The flat steel plate, let's say, is a foot square, and the pipe or shaft is welded to the center of the plate. You slide a couple of 45-lb. plates down the pipe and let them rest on the plate below. Now the plates are well-secured. You can also drill holes through the pipe if you want to stick a three-inch-long bolt through the pipe just above the plates and screw a nut on it. You can drill these holes every two inches up to a foot or two feet high above the bottom of the flat plate.

Now imagine two 45-lb. plates on the bottom of this five-foot high pipe. Then imagine you grabbing the pipe close to the top, tipping the pipe to waist-high and grabbing the pipe with your other hand about two feet above the 45-lb. plates, and lifting the whole load off the ground like you would lift a shovel full of dirt. Lift it and level it out. Lift it waist-high and make it parallel with the ground.

In your mind, visualize the stress this will throw on the body. It is tremendous. Then to make things even harder, swing the weight from out in front of your body to the side of your body, then behind your body and then all the way back to the front again. We'll call this one rep. And if you really want to make things tough, when you get back to the front, pull the weight up high overhead, then down and level it out, and then swing it back around behind you again. It would be like scooping up a shovel of snow and swinging the shovel head behind your body, then back to the front of your body, then up over your head with the snow landing behind you. This puts a tremendous strain on all kinds of muscles from head to toes.

I did nothing but practice this lift every day for two weeks. And even though I didn't practice any other lifts during these two weeks, when I went back to my other lifts, about 30 different lifts, I literally gained strength in every one of my other lifts. It was unbelievable. The routine I used for those two weeks was 20 sets of two reps every day with a moderately heavy weight. That would be 10 sets of two reps each side.

I used a weight just heavy enough that I was slightly tired after two reps. Then I would take about a 30-second to a minute-and-a-half rest in between each set. I worked it left side, then right side, alternating sides between each set. If a minute-and-a-half rest isn't enough time for you to get to the next set, you're using too heavy a weight. This should take you 30 to 40 minutes to complete the whole workout. When you are done, your whole body will feel a rush.

What I do is start with a weight that feels moderately heavy and use this same weight day in and day out until it feels moderately light. When this happens, you know your body has adapted. Then you add 10 lb. and do this day in and day out, and when that weight feels moderately light, you add weight again, and so forth and so on. Always listen to the feel of the weight. Your body and mind will always tell you when to add weight. Learn to feel the weight.

Never jump to a heavier weight before you're ready, because if you go beyond your limits, you will fail. You will fail mentally and physically if you get too impatient and jump to heavier weight too fast. Always learn to feel the weight and stay within your limits, because if you keep jumping ahead too fast and the weight gets beyond your limit, your mind will fail and you shall become scared

Steve Justa fires up a shovel lift with 210 lb.

of the weight, not to mention that it is a good way to get hurt. So believe me when I say stay within your limits. This way you'll look forward to your workouts and have fun doing it. If you go beyond your limits too quick, you'll dread your workouts, and you'll fail.

Now the reason the shovel or pitchfork lift is so awesome is because it works so many muscles. When the weight is in front of your body, it stresses all the muscles on your back side and your toes, feet, and calves. When the weight is out to the side, it hits all your side muscles—side waist, thigh, and hip; and when the weight is behind you it works all your front muscles, front stomach, front shin, front thigh, front chest. When you raise the weight to head high or overhead, it hits all your upper body muscles. And when you swing the weight from front to back and to the front, you're working all your sideways twisting muscles—muscles that 99% of today's lifters neglect. These sideways rotator muscles are truly powerful muscles when developed.

This shovel or pitchfork lift is truly a king of all the lifts. I believe it directly works more muscles than any other lift except maybe the barrel lift. I think though it might even outdo the old barrel lift. This would be a great lift for any athlete in any sport, and it is truly a great lift for the person interested in developing super strength and super coordination and stamina.

My grandpa used to throw hay bales into a nine-foot-high hay mound with a specially-built steel pitchfork, and he had tremendous bodily strength and huge shoulders and back. And he used to sometimes work all day doing this. I believe, conceive, achieve, and never doubt the benefits of truly hard work. To give an example of the strength this lift gave my grandpa, he was hauling grain to the elevator one day in a truck and was waiting in a long line to dump his grain. He'd been waiting there for over an hour already and was really frustrated when another farmer jumped in front of him, cutting him off with another truck.

Well, Grandpa got so mad, he went up and with one arm, pulled this other character out through his truck window and held him off the ground by his coat collar, with the arm away from his body. And the guy was dangling in the air with his feet off the ground, and Gramps was holding him with one hand—a 200-lb. man off the ground with one hand. Now that is a true exhibition of super strength.

So, to all my fellow lifters out there who like my way of thinking on this lift, good luck and give it hell.

CHAPTER 11

Barrel Lifting

Let me ask you a question: What would be the best lift to develop all around strength? Put a simpler way, what is the hardest kind of weight to lift? An awkward bulk weight is the hardest because it places extreme stress on the muscles from the severest angles which crisscross the frame, and automatically ties in all the big powerful muscles fastest, and the small stabilizer muscles all at the same time.

My philosophy of bulk and strength is the heavier the weights you lift, or the more repetitions you can do, all tie in together, making you stronger and bigger, so the answer to getting big and strong is MORE: more reps with light weight, or more weight, or both. For example, a lot of powerlifters do ten reps or less in the squat, and the best probably do 800 pounds for ten reps, weighing probably 300 pounds bodyweight. This is 11,000 pounds of weight he has moved in ten reps.

On the other hand, take the Japanese sumo wrestler who weighs 400 pounds, does 400 reps with just his own bodyweight, and he has done 40,000 pounds of work. Both men are extremely strong but yet took two different paths to reach the same end. This leads us to the barrel lift. If you stick with this lift for two to four years, you will develop big, strong, powerful muscles throughout the whole body.

The first step is to find a barrel. You might get an empty oil barrel, 15 or 30 gallons, if you go to oil companies, gas stations or the city dump, or you could buy or obtain a beer keg from a distributing company, or you could have a fiberglass model made, or go to a blacksmith shop and have them make you one out of pipe casing, put ends on the pipe and a door on the side. Use your imagination and you'll come up with something. Eat good, well-balanced diets. Get a thick rug, blanket, rubber mat or old tire to set your barrel on so you don't smash the sides in. Use gravel, rocks, sand, dirt or water for weight in your barrel. Get loose fitting clothes and a tight fitting pair of leather gloves.

The Barrel Lift Workout

You will practice every other day, three days a week, taking Saturday and Sunday off. No more, no less. Practice no longer than an hour and a half each session. You will do 50 repetitions in each lift, no less. Pick a weight you can do at least 50 reps with in

Steve Justa demonstrates lift #1, Shouldering the Barrel.

exercises #1 and #4. You will add five pounds of weight to your barrel every Sunday and you will still maintain your 50 reps. If for some reason you do not maintain your 50 reps during any one of your three weekly workouts, you will punish yourself by not adding your five pounds for that week.

Left, Steve Justa demonstrates lift #2, Barrel Squat, and right, lift #3, Barrel Deadlift.

If you are successful every week for a straight year, you will have gained 255 pounds of all-around, useful, awkward strength which is really a spectacular feat in itself. You could take a fully-loaded keg of beer and play with it because it would weigh only 167 pounds and who knows: After four years of training, you might even be able to body slam big John Stud.

Exercises

#1 Shouldering Barrel. Stand erect with barrel on shoulder, lower to ground and stand erect again. Do 50 reps each side. Lower the barrel in the same position as you lift.

#2 Barrel Squat. Shoulder barrel and squat up and down all the way. Do 50 reps each side.

#3 Barrel Deadlift. Grab barrel by rims and lift to waist as many reps as possible. Do one set only.

#4 Barrel Bear Hug. Set barrel on end, bend down and bear hug barrel. Stand erect and hold barrel in bear hug position as long as possible. Do one set.

I'll guarantee you, you'll be tired when you're done if you've pushed yourself to the limit. You'll probably be sore the first week. So, good luck, work hard, eat good and maybe some day you'll be able to lift a 500-pound barrel. That would be awesome.

As an addition to the 50-rep philosophy, there are other strategies as well in the barrel lift. The 50-rep philosophy I mentioned earlier builds tremendous endurance and is really tough, and you must have patience. This routine works effectively if the barrel lift is the only lift you practice, but if you do other lifts as well and want to work it into your routine, here are a few strategies for you to think about.

#1 Barrel Bear Hug and Hold. Bear hug your barrel from the ground and stand erect with the barrel, holding it against your chest. Hold the barrel until you start getting tired. Set the barrel down, rest two minutes and do this again. Do five sets of these holds.

#2 Barrel Bear Hug Lift. Go to the bear hug again and pick up the barrel, hold it against the chest, then set it down, and then bear hug it up to your chest again, and keep repping out this way until you get tired. Again, use a weight you can get about 10 reps with, and keep at this weight until you can get 20 reps. When you can get 20 reps, add more weight. Do two sets of these, then go to shouldering the barrel.

#3 Shouldering Barrel. Remember in shouldering the barrel that we rotate working the right shoulder, then the left shoulder. To pull the barrel up to the right shoulder, grab the bottom of the barrel with your left hand, under the bottom rim. Tilt the barrel slightly to the right and lean it slightly forward. Bear hug the barrel with your right arm, and bend your knees slightly. Now tense your muscles and give a tremendous heave and pull the barrel from the ground to your shoulder and up on your shoulder in one motion. If you can't get it from the ground to your shoulder in one continuous motion, you're using too much weight. Do 10 reps on your right

side, rest a couple of minutes, then do 10 reps on your left side. Then, when you can get 20 reps, add more weight, five to ten pounds.

#4 Barrel Deadlift. Lifting the barrel by the rims to the waist builds tremendous arm, wrist and hand strength. Do two sets of 10 reps, and when you can get 20 reps, add more weight.

Steve Justa demonstrates lift #4, Bear Hug and Hold.

#5 Barrel Squat. Load barrel up on your shoulder and squat up and down 10 reps right side, then rest a couple minutes and do ten reps left side. When you can get 20 reps, add more weight.

#6 Barrel Throws. This is also a very good series of exercises not shown in the photographs. Make yourself a sandbox four feet wide and eight feet long or 12 feet long. Make the sand about four inches deep. Now tie a rope across the middle of the sandbox about chest high, anchored to stakes along each side. Now grab your barrel and throw it over the rope to the other side in various positions and styles. You can stand at right angles to the rope and grab the barrel by the rims and throw it over sideways, from the left and then from the right. Then you can throw it over your shoulder with your back to the rope. You can throw it over the

rope while you are facing the rope. Just use your imagination and throw the barrel over the rope in as many different styles as you can think of.

This works so many different muscles from different angles. Throw your barrel over this rope 20 times, and when you figure you can do it 20 times with more weight, add more weight. Rest about 30 seconds in between throws. I guarantee you, you'll use muscles you never even knew you had in this workout.

This barrel lifting is tremendous training for wrestlers or footballers or for the strength athlete that wants all around strength, power, coordination and stamina. If you are doing other lifts as well and want to supplement your training with barrel lifting, I would do this routine once or twice a week. If you're only concentrating on barrel lifting, I would do this routine every day or every other day, depending on how your feel or how hard your day job is.

Another plan of attack is to do each lift for two or three single reps every day, in addition to all your other lifts. Or if you're just barrel lifting, the same will work also, but when you're doing these singles you must perform these lifts every day and start with a medium heavy weight and stay with this same weight until it feels medium light, then add weight and proceed. And as with all lifts, you must stay within your limits. Go beyond your limits too fast and your progress will come to a grinding halt.

CHAPTER 12

Training Philosophy and Attack Plan

#1. Nutrition equals food plus water and is very important.
Your body is like an engine; if it doesn't get enough fuel it doesn't
run. Drink a lot of water or products that have water in them.
Water has oxygen and about 100 different minerals in it. It builds
strong bones and cleans your system out, plus it gets oxygen in
your body. To lift heavy weights you need strong bones.

Try to eat green salad, apples, carrots, celery, parsley, seeds,
beans, and nuts; try to eat these uncooked *at least once or twice a
week*. And maybe a steak, medium rare. These uncooked foods
will give your body all the vitamins and enzymes it needs. The
water, at least a gallon or two a day, will give your body all the
minerals it needs. The medium rare or rare steak contains chemi-
cals in it that will greatly accelerate your muscle strength.

Then, just most of the time, eat your favorite foods or what
you crave. And fill up the plate. Eating what sounds good and
tastes good, and a lot of it, until you're good and full is very, very
important. If you follow this philosophy, you can't go wrong.

#2. Fast one day a week. This is optional, but good to do
once in a while. Once a week, go one day without eating any solid
food, at least 20-24 hours. This will clean the body out. This gets
all the toxins and poisons out of your body. This cleans your intes-
tines out. This will make you feel good, and will make your body
more efficient and stronger. It's like spraying carburetor cleaner in
a dirty carburetor. This is very important. There is a basketball
player in the N.B.A. who is about 43 years old, and he fasts once a
week. He has had a longer career in the N.B.A. than anyone else,
and he moves like a young kid. He's never had any injuries either.

And he's been pounding up and down that basketball floor for over 20 years. Hakeem Alijahone fasts one day a week also. He's the center for the Houston Rockets, and he is in great shape also.

#3. Strength, power, and speed are what you want. These all go hand in hand. Each one helps build the other. Vasily Alexeev, the super heavyweight Russian weightlifter, weighed 370 lb. And he could do a standing broad jump over 10 feet.

Speed—if you move a light weight fast, it becomes heavier; the G-force factor kicks in. For example, say you can lift 200 lb. off the ground to your mid-thigh easily, but you try it again, only this time you pull it as fast as you can. This time it will feel like 300 lb. because even though you moved the same weight the same distance, you moved it a lot faster the same distance, so you have generated more power. And the more power you can generate, the more strength you will have.

Power is the amount or work you can do in a certain time. Let's say, for example, if you can carry 200 lb. on your shoulders for a hundred yards in 30 seconds' time, you have produced so much power. But if you can carry 200 lb. on your shoulders a hundred yards in 15 seconds, you've generated almost twice as much power. And the more power you can generate, the more strength you will have also.

Strength is the total of speed plus power plus endurance. *So the faster and longer you move a light weight, the easier it will be to move a heavy weight.* Never ever forget this; this is very important. Strength is the ability to hold or move great amounts of weight.

#4. A positive attitude, will power, consistency, belief, visualization, sacrifice—these are the mental tools you will use to build your strength, power, and speed. Each one builds on the other, and they all go hand in hand to create momentum. It's like a snowball rolling down a hill; it starts out small but the farther down the hill it gets, it gets bigger and faster and carries more force. The mind works the same way. The harder you work or the more consistently you work, the more you feel as if you deserve to reap

the harvest. And the more you feel you deserve it, the more you will see it in your mind. The more you see it, the more you believe it. And the more you believe, the more force you have.

Never doubt the power of belief—it is great. It will give you all the answers to all the questions. And when it comes to gaining strength, *consistency builds momentum and momentum builds strength*. Never forget this. This is important. And if you really believe you can, chances are you will. If you believe, your mind will show you how.

#5. Training includes experimenting; learning to listen to your body; setting long range goals and short range day-to-day goals; building coordination; and building confidence. What do you want? Conceive, believe, achieve, practice, practice, practice. Hundreds of routes, hundreds of angles, hundreds of paths can lead to the same destination. Focus, concentrate, get determined, most of all start thinking and doing. How much is too much, how much is too little? Just because somebody says so, doesn't make it so. Everybody is different, so almost everybody will train differently. What are you used to, what can you get used to, how much can you get used to? I will give you my basic philosophy.

#6. Establish a base. What would happen if you took a normal person and put him or her in an Iron Man Triathlon—swim two miles, bicycle 125 miles, run 26 miles. I'll tell you: If you put a normal, untrained person in a race like that and he managed to finish it, he'd be so sore he couldn't walk for two weeks. But you can put a trained triathlete champion through the same race, and he probably won't even be stiff the next day and can probably run the same race all over again the next day if he really had to. So you must understand this—this is important.

To plan your weightlifting strategy for what is ahead, you have to look and pay attention to what is behind: You have to build a base. Again you have the snowball effect. Again momentum. An amateur can't train like a professional, because you have to lay the foundation before you can build the house. This means patience, persistence, consistency, work, and, above all, this means you have to learn to listen.

#7. *Listen to your body.* Think this way: stronger, tougher, longer, farther, faster, heavier, more repetitions, lighter faster, lighter farther, heavier once one day, heavier twice the next, heavier lighter shorter, heavier lighter farther, heavier lighter farther faster, then the heavier lighter has turned into the lighter farther. Do you see what I'm trying to say. You build the base over and over again, layer by layer. And while you keep striving to build endurance, strength, power, speed, you must listen to your body. Keep in touch, it is trying to tell you. *Gradually let it build*, little by little, bit by bit, like the snowball down the hill as it gains momentum. Too much work for a weak base is disastrous; the house will fall. Remember, you should always feel stronger after your training than before you started. If you feel weak after a training session, you've overdone it.

#8. *Lifting strategies.* Start with weights that feel fairly light, and work and build up from there. Try to work the legs and hips — the front, back, and sides of the legs and hips. Try to work the front, stomach, side, waist, back, chest, shoulders, biceps, triceps, forearms, hands, feet, ankles, and neck. Then after a couple of weeks of working with light weights, you should be tough enough to start adding weight, distance, or reps, or speed, or all three or four, depending on what kind of lift you are practicing.

Remember, *the center of all your strength and power is in your lower back and hips and upper legs*, so on all lifts, always concentrate on keeping these muscles tensed and your stomach tensed. To push a heavy weight overhead, you must have a strong back.

After your two-week break-in period, you need to jump to weights that feel medium-heavy to you. An example of medium heavy is a weight you can do a minimum of 8-10 reps with. Say, for example, you have a barbell on the floor and you can pull it to your mid-thigh, eight times up and down, with a second or two rest in between each rep. If you're going from the floor over your head each time, you'll want to rest about 30 seconds between each rep. *Now the key is to have the patience to stay with this medium-heavy weight every day until it actually starts to feel light, even if you have to stay at that same weight for a month.* When it feels light to you, you are ready to add weight to your exercise; in this way you let the body adapt.

#9. Think smart. Always try to feel stronger after your work-out than before you started. In this way you will assure yourself a lot of reserve energy from workout to workout and make good progress in your lifts. Learn to feel what your body is telling you and remember, *a little bit every day is a whole lot smarter and more productive than a whole lot one day a week*. This is *consistency* and *momentum*. A little bit every day adds up fast over time, believe me. So choose the lifts you want to do. If you do six or seven lifts a day, you'll want to cut way back on your sets because you're working so many lifts a day. If you just do one lift a day, you can work it a lot more, but that's your choice.

It is impossible to tie all of these different kinds of workouts into one package because everyone's body is at a different level of fitness, and some people might want speed strength without size. Some people might just want brute power and strength. Each different lift and workout gives you something different in the way of strength, speed, coordination, power and endurance. Look at the Training Guide for Strength Athletes, Group A and Group B at the end of this chapter to see which lifts work best for your sport.

Now, to put bodyweight on and get huge like Paul Anderson was, do about ten different lifts, like squats, half squats, quarter squats, half deadlifts, breaking-off-the-floor deadlifts, benches, overhead presses, overhead push presses to eye level, overhead dumbells, curls, stuff like this, and work to pump the maximum amount of blood into each muscle in a minimum amount of time. Train every day and eat like a horse, getting a lot of sugar and protein into the body.

Or you can train like Arthur Saxon did: Do 30 different exer-cises, using singles, not reps. He did certain exercises every day, but in the course of a week, he probably did 30 altogether. He had maximum body strength with minimum bodyweight.

You must learn to think for yourself. Listen to your body and figure out what you want, then come up with a strategy to get what you want. I've supplied you with all kinds of different strategies, and they will all work if you stick with them. Now it's up to you to figure out which is right for you, or you can even come up with your own.

The best thing to do is a little bit of everything from time to time, but for most of the time, stick to the workout strategy and the lifts you choose on a consistent basis. When it comes time to lift, lift, don't talk. You'll never get stronger thinking about training—you must train.

The body will adapt to almost any workout if you have patience and give it time, and when your body does adapt, that's when you'll start making progress. All great lifters learn to generate great consistency and patience. Gaining great strength is purely a matter of *will power*. You'll get as strong as your will power will push you, pure and simple. Gaining great strength is a matter of asserting your will power on a steady and consistent basis. It is far better to do less work on a consistent basis than to do a whole lot of work from time to time.

The best advice is to do as much as you can without ever making yourself tired. Learn to listen to your body. Always try to end your workouts feeling stronger than you did before you started. In this way you'll have plenty of strength.

Training Guide for Strength Athletes—Group A

	Football	Wrestling	Baseball	Basketball	Surfing	Strong man	Tennis	Hockey	Boxing	Cycling	Track
1. Bent press.	X	X	X	X	X	X	X	X	X	X	X
2. Walking with barbell on one shoulder with shoulder pad, or sandbag on shoulder.	X	X		X		X		X	X	X	
3. Walking with barbell behind neck, both shoulders.	X	X				X	X	X	X		X
4. Running with barbell behind neck.	X	X	X	X	X	X	X	X	X		X
5. Running with sandbag on shoulder.	X	X	X			X	X	X	X		X
6. Barrel lift from ground to shoulder.		X	X	X	X		X		X		X
7. Hand and thigh lift and hold or for reps.	X	X	X	X			X	X			
8. Back lift for reps, or back lift and hold.	X	X	X			X		X			X
9. Barrel lift from ground to knee height, hold for time at knee height.	X	X	X			X		X	X	X	X
10. Rock lift off mid-thigh-high support and carry for distance.	X	X				X		X			
11. Rock lift off ground to waist- or chest-high and carry for distance.	X			X		X					
12. Rock lift off ground bent over row, rowing rock to chest, wide stance.	X	X			X	X					
13. Good morning barbell exercise with extremely wide stance.	X	X	X	X	X	X	X	X			
14. Barrel deadlift by rims.	X	X	X			X			X		
15. Barrel or rock bear-hug lift from ground, hold for time.	X	X	X			X		X			
16. Barbell off chairs or 25-inch blocks, two-hand pull into shoulder from the side, hands overlapping.	X	X	X	X	X	X	X	X	X	X	X
17. Barbell lift off rack, two hands, hold starting position of overhead press.	X	X		X		X			X		
18. Barbell jerk overhead, hold for time.	X	X	X	X		X			X		
19. Barbell overhead press, turn side to side while arms are extended overhead.	X	X	X	X	X	X	X	X	X	X	X
20. Barbell shoulder raise off rack for reps or for timed hold, with pads on shoulders.	X	X	X	X	X	X	X	X	X	X	X
21. Barbell raise off rack behind neck, standing straight, turn legs in and out, standing on heel of foot.	X	X	X	X	X	X	X	X	X		
22. Barbell lift off rack in toe stand position, hold for time.	X	X	X	X	X	X	X	X	X	X	X
23. Barbell straight-legged, round-back lift off rack, hold in round back position.	X	X	X			X		X		X	
24. Barbell lift off rack behind neck or in front press position, standing off balance.	X	X	X	X	X	X	X		X	X	X
25. Barbell lockout lift off rack, hold behind neck for time.	X	X				X			X		
26. Half squat, extreme front lean.	X	X	X	X	X	X	X	X			

Training Guide for Strength Athletes—Group A

	Football	Wrestling	Baseball	Basket ball	Surfing	Strong man	Tennis	Hockey	Boxing	Cycling	Track
27. Regular squat.	X	X				X		X			
28. Barrel squat on shoulder.	X	X	X			X	X	X	X		
29. Rock lift off waist-high support and hold.	X	X	X	X		X	X	X	X	X	X
30. Weight plate finger curl, two hand.	X	X	X	X		X	X	X	X	X	X
31. Barbell wrist curl.	X	X	X			X		X			
32. Steel suitcase lift between legs, one hand.		X	X	X		X	X	X	X	X	X
33. Steel suitcase lift and hold to side, one hand.		X	X	X	X	X	X	X	X	X	X
34. Steel suitcase lift and walk, one hand.		X	X	X	X	X	X	X	X	X	X
35. Steel suitcase lift and run, one hand.	X	X	X	X	X	X	X	X	X	X	X
36. Kettlebell thumb hang overhead press from top of head, one hand.	X	X	X	X		X	X	X	X	X	X
37. Kettlebell one-hand swing between legs to chest high, alternating hands at top of swing.	X	X	X	X		X	X	X	X	X	X
38. Kettlebell two-hand swing between legs to waist high.	X	X	X	X	X	X	X	X	X		
39. Kettlebell swing outside of legs, one hand.	X	X	X	X	X	X	X	X	X	X	X
40. Weight plates two-hand pinch grip, palms down, held at chest height.		X	X	X		X	X	X	X	X	X
41. Weight plates chest squeeze.	X	X		X		X		X			
42. Deadlift barbell to knee, wide stance.											
43. Deadlift, breaking weight off floor two inches, narrow stance.	X	X	X			X		X			
44. Sledgehammer handle lifts, one hand, various positions.	X	X		X		X	X	X	X	X	X
45. Shovel lift waist level, turn 180 degrees from front to back to front.	X	X	X	X	X	X	X	X	X	X	X
46. Thick-handle dumbbell lift between legs, hold for time, one hand.			X							X	
47. Neck bridge press with barbell.	X	X		X		X		X	X		
48. Overhead shovel lift, front, side, and back.	X	X	X	X	X	X	X	X	X	X	X
49. Barbell lunge between legs to front.	X	X	X	X	X	X	X	X	X	X	X
50. Barbell lunge between legs to side.	X	X	X	X	X	X	X	X	X	X	X
51. Steel hand grippers for reps and holds, with fingers and thumbs sideways.	X	X	X	X		X	X	X	X	X	
52. Roman chair layback and hold parallel to ground, with weight held above head.	X	X	X	X	X	X	X	X	X	X	X
53. Push-up, holding weight on back.	X	X	X			X					
54. Bent arm deadlift, hold palms up.		X	X			X		X	X	X	X
55. Barbell finger lifting and holds with various combinations of fingers.	X	X	X	X	X	X	X	X	X	X	X
56. Off-center barbell clean and press.	X	X	X	X		X	X	X	X	X	X
57. Shovel lift bent arm curl and hold.				X	X	X	X		X	X	X
58. Punching with dumbbell.				X		X			X	X	X

Training Guide for Strength Athletes—Group A

	Football	Wrestling	Baseball	Basketball	Surfing	Strong man	Tennis	Hockey	Boxing	Cycling	Track
59. Steel brick throw with trap door on end to add weight (e.g. with lead shot) when needed.	X			X		X	X		X	X	X
60. Scissor walk sideways, dragging weight with hands, standing position, weight hooked to chain.	X	X	X		X	X	X	X	X	X	X
61. Barrel or rock lifting from ground to waist starting from kneeling position.		X				X					
62. Barrel or rock lifting from ground to waist, kneeling on one foot and one knee touching ground.	X	X				X					
63. Weight drag backwards with hands, standing position.	X	X		X	X	X	X	X	X	X	
64. Weight drag forward with harness.	X	X	X	X		X	X	X	X	X	X
65. Isometrics 2- to 3-minute holds.		X	X	X		X	X	X	X	X	X
66. Isometrics 7-second 90% power holds.	X	X	X	X		X	X	X	X	X	X
67. Frog walk with barbell behind neck.	X	X		X	X	X	X	X	X		X
68. Frog jumping with barbell behind neck.	X	X		X	X	X	X	X	X		X
69. Rock-bottom squat trunk rotation and spin, barbell behind neck.	X	X		X	X	X	X	X	X	X	X
70. Lifting and holding weight for one minute, holds in various positions.	X	X		X	X	X	X	X	X	X	X
71. G-force training.	X	X		X	X	X	X	X	X	X	X
72. Thick-handle barbell training.	X	X	X			X	X			X	
73. Hammer pounding.		X		X	X	X	X		X	X	X
74. Barbell deadlift full range, narrow stance.	X	X			X	X	X		X		X
75. Barbell deadlift full range, extremely wide stance.	X					X		X			
76. Power clean barbell to chest from floor.	X	X	X	X		X	X		X	X	X
77. Clean and jerk barbell squat-style.		X			X	X			X		
78. Overhead standing jerk with barbell.	X			X		X					
79. Power clean and jerk with barbell.	X				X	X			X		X
80. Power clean barbell from knee to chest.	X					X					X
81. Power clean barbell from waist to chest.					X	X					
82. Snatch barbell squat-style from floor to overhead.					X	X	X	X	X		X
83. Snatch one-arm dumbbell squat-style from floor to overhead.	X	X	X	X	X	X	X	X	X		X
84. Kettlebell toss across front of hips, standing, from right side to left, back and forth.	X	X		X	X	X	X	X	X		X
85. Kettlebell throw standing, one arm to rear.	X	X	X	X	X	X	X	X	X	X	X
86. Kettlebell throw standing, one arm to front.	X		X	X	X	X	X	X	X	X	X
87. Walking with weight vest for one to five miles.	X	X		X	X	X	X		X	X	X
88. Teeth lifting with weight.	X	X	X	X	X	X	X	X	X	X	X

Training Guide for Strength Athletes—Group B

	Wrist wrestling	Rock climbing	Triathlon	Gymnastics	Swimming	Volleyball
1. Bent press.	X			X	X	X
2. Walking with barbell on one shoulder with shoulder pad, or sandbag on shoulder.		X			X	
3. Walking with barbell behind neck, both shoulders.		X		X	X	
4. Running with barbell behind neck.		X	X	X		X
5. Running with sandbag on shoulder.		X	X	X	X	
6. Barrel lift from ground to shoulder.		X		X		
7. Hand and thigh lift and hold or for reps.	X					X
8. Back lift for reps, or back lift and hold.	X		X	X	X	
9. Barrel lift from ground to knee height, hold for time at knee height.	X	X		X		
10. Rock lift off mid-thigh-high support and carry for distance.					X	
11. Rock lift off ground to waist- or chest-high and carry for distance.						
12. Rock lift off ground bent over row, rowing rock to chest, wide stance.	X	X			X	
13. Good morning barbell exercise with extremely wide stance.				X	X	
14. Barrel deadlift by rims.	X	X		X	X	X
15. Barrel or rock bear-hug lift from ground, hold for time.	X	X				
16. Barbell off chairs or 25-inch blocks, two-hand pull into shoulder from the side, hands overlapping.		X				
17. Barbell lift off rack, two hands, hold starting position of overhead press.	X	X	X	X	X	X
18. Barbell jerk overhead, hold for time.	X			X	X	
19. Barbell overhead press, turn side to side while arms are extended overhead.	X	X		X		X
20. Barbell shoulder raise off rack for reps or for timed hold, with pads on shoulders.	X	X	X	X	X	X
21. Barbell raise off rack behind neck, standing straight, turn legs in and out, standing on heel of foot.	X	X	X	X	X	X
22. Barbell lift off rack in toe stand position, hold for time.		X	X	X	X	X
23. Barbell straight-legged, round-back lift off rack, hold in round back position.				X		
24. Barbell lift off rack behind neck or in front press position, standing off balance.	X	X	X	X	X	X
25. Barbell lockout lift off rack, hold behind neck for time.		X				
26. Half squat, extreme front lean.						

Training Guide for Strength Athletes—Group B

	Wrist wrestling	Rock climbing	Triathlon	Gymnastics	Swimming	Volley ball
27. Regular squat.						
28. Barrel squat on shoulder.		X		X		
29. Rock lift off waist-high support and hold.	X	X		X		X
30. Weight plate finger curl, two hand.	X	X		X		X
31. Barbell wrist curl.						
32. Steel suitcase lift between legs, one hand.	X	X	X	X	X	X
33. Steel suitcase lift and hold to side, one hand.	X	X	X	X	X	X
34. Steel suitcase lift and walk, one hand.	X	X	X	X	X	X
35. Steel suitcase lift and run, one hand.	X	X	X	X	X	X
36. Kettlebell thumb hang overhead press from top of head, one hand.	X	X		X		
37. Kettlebell one-hand swing between legs to chest high, alternating hands at top of swing.	X	X	X	X	X	X
38. Kettlebell two-hand swing between legs to waist high.	X	X		X		
39. Kettlebell swing outside of legs, one hand.	X	X	X	X	X	X
40. Weight plates two-hand pinch grip, palms down, held at chest height.	X		X	X	X	X
41. Weight plates chest squeeze.	X	X		X	X	
42. Deadlift barbell to knee, wide stance, weight ahead of barbell.						
43. Deadlift, breaking weight off floor two inches, narrow stance.						
44. Sledgehammer handle lifts, one hand, various positions.	X	X		X	X	X
45. Shovel lift waist level, turn 180 degrees from front to back to front.	X	X	X	X	X	X
46. Thick-handle dumbbell lift between legs, hold for time, one hand.	X	X				
47. Neck bridge press with barbell.		X		X	X	
48. Overhead shovel lift, front, side, and back.	X	X	X	X	X	X
49. Barbell lunge between legs to front.		X	X	X	X	X
50. Barbell lunge between legs to side.		X	X	X	X	X
51. Steel hand grippers for reps and holds, with fingers and thumbs sideways.	X	X		X		
52. Roman chair layback and hold parallel to ground, with weight held above head.	X	X	X	X	X	X
53. Push-up, holding weight on back.	X	X	X	X	X	
54. Bent arm deadlift, hold palms up.	X	X	X			
55. Barbell finger lifting and holds with various combinations of fingers.	X	X		X	X	
56. Off-center barbell clean and press.	X	X		X	X	X
57. Shovel lift bent arm curl and hold.	X	X		X	X	X
58. Punching with dumbbell.	X	X		X	X	X

Training Guide for Strength Athletes—Group B

	Wrist wrestling	Rock climbing	Triathlon	Gymnastics	Swimming	Volleyball
59. Steel brick throw with trap door on end to add weight (e.g. with lead shot) when needed.						X
60. Scissor walk sideways, dragging weight with hands, standing position, weight hooked to chain.					X	X
61. Barrel or rock lifting from ground to waist starting from kneeling position.				X	X	X
62. Barrel or rock lifting from ground to waist, kneeling on one foot and one knee touching ground.						
63. Weight drag backwards with hands, standing position.						
64. Weight drag forward with harness.						
65. Isometrics 2- to 3-minute holds.	X	X	X	X	X	X
66. Isometrics 7-second 90% power holds.	X	X	X	X	X	X
67. Frog walk with barbell behind neck.		X				
68. Frog jumping with barbell behind neck.				X		
69. Rock-bottom squat trunk rotation and spin, barbell behind neck.			X	X	X	X
70. Lifting and holding weight for one minute, holds in various positions.	X			X	X	X
71. G-force training.	X	X	X	X	X	X
72. Thick-handle barbell training.	X	X				
73. Hammer pounding.	X	X			X	X
74. Barbell deadlift full range, narrow stance.	X	X				
75. Barbell deadlift full range, extremely wide stance.						
76. Power clean barbell to chest from floor.				X	X	X
77. Clean and jerk barbell squat-style.				X		
78. Overhead standing jerk with barbell.	X			X		
79. Power clean and jerk with barbell.			X	X	X	
80. Power clean barbell from knee to chest.				X	X	X
81. Power clean barbell from waist to chest.	X			X	X	X
82. Snatch barbell squat-style from floor to overhead.				X		X
83. Snatch one-arm dumbbell squat-style from floor to overhead.			X	X		
84. Kettlebell toss across front of hips, standing, from right side to left, back and forth.		X	X	X	X	X
85. Kettlebell throw standing, one arm to rear.		X	X	X	X	
86. Kettlebell throw standing, one arm to front.	X	X	X			
87. Walking with weight vest for one to five miles.	X	X	X	X	X	X
88. Teeth lifting with weight.						

Quick Description of Lifts

1. Barbell is standing on end. Pressing hand will be in the exact center of bar, other hand right below. Rock barbell to shoulder, put elbow as far back as it will go. Bend sideways and forward until body is parallel with ground, straighten arm and then stand up with weight. One of the best all-around lifts ever invented.

2. A two-inch solid steel bar works the best. This lift hits all the muscles on the side of the body.

3. A two-inch solid steel bar works the best here, too. Walking with barbell behind neck builds tremendous strength throughout the whole body. Good all-around lift.

4. Directly hits feet, ankles, knees, and groin. Good lift for any athlete who has to move body around powerfully and quickly.

5. Hits side muscles of body. Good endurance and power movement.

6. Barrel lift from ground to shoulder is another excellent all-around lift. Will tire out more muscles more quickly than any other lift. Builds strength through whole body—front, sides, and back.

7. The hand and thigh or quarter deadlift is an excellent hip and upper thigh builder, as well as trapezius builder, and to a slightly lesser degree, the whole body. A solid cold-rolled bar of 1-1/2 inches in diameter works the best, with the bar mounted solidly to stands or barrels that hold the weight. Fifty to 70 reps of this exercise will leave your whole body feeling like a rock, if you use 70% of your max. Excellent tendon and ligament strength builder.

8. The back lift is a true test of leg and hip strength. This is where the body is under a platform, legs slightly bent, back flat against platform parallel to ground, arms slightly bent and resting on stool, and weight is raised straight up an inch or two. Excellent tendon and ligament strength builder through whole body. Excellent all-around strength builder.

9. This backbreaker hits side muscles, back, back legs, hips, arm biceps, forearms, and hands and wrists. Good power and strength builder. Another good all-around lift.

10. This really hits the forward thrusting motion of the legs and hips, and the lower back. Good power builder.

11. Really hits hips, legs, back, forearms, grip, and chest.

12. Bent row with big rock or chunk of concrete really hits all back muscles hard, also biceps, hips and hamstrings.

13. This hits the hips and hamstrings very intensely, plus it gives you a lot of pulling power from the ground. Good assistance exercise for rock lifting or barrel lifting. Barbell is behind the neck, with your legs spread as wide as possible, then bend parallel to ground and up. Also hits the neck hard.

14. Hits all the muscles on the back side of the body, as well as hands, wrists, forearms and biceps, triceps, and chest. Good power builder.

15. Hits chest, arms, wrists, hands, and all muscles on the back side of the body.

16. Place barbell on two chairs. Stand at middle and grab bar with both hands overlapping in center. Bend over and to the side; pull bar in and up to shoulder height. Great movement for arm wrestlers; also hits side muscles extremely hard.

17. This is where you pick a heavy weight off a rack in the overhead press position. But instead of pressing it, you just pick it up and hold it for time. Hits the upper body extremely hard, especially triceps, chest, forearm, and traps.

18. Builds good neck and trap and triceps strength as well as wrist and shoulder.

19. This slight spinning motion back and forth while the bar is overhead works a lot of stabilizer muscles in the back, chest and shoulder. Excellent for swimmers, basketball players, or baseball players.

20. A two-inch bar with pad works best for this exercise. Builds extreme shoulder and side body power; also a super trapezius builder. Excellent for footballers.

21. Hold and lift barbell off rack behind neck. Pull toes up slightly standing straight; now spin legs so toes touch, then spin outwards so toes point out to the sides. Builds hip and leg control strength. Good for a running back in football.

22. Toe raise stands build tremendous foot, ankle, and calf strength. Good for any athlete because all body movement starts with the foot. To be strong in this area is a top priority in my mind for any athlete.

23. You stand in the power rack slightly bent forward at the waist with back rounded. Pick up barbell in power rack, bar behind neck, and hold for time. Keep legs straight. Excellent back strength and spine builder.

24. This is where you're in the power rack, and you lift the barbell either with hands in front as in the overhead press position or lift with barbell behind neck. But the hard part is you lift off-center, once to the left and once to the right. Really builds upper body twisting and torque muscles as well as biceps and triceps and shoulder. Good power and strength builder. I also recommend this for any football player or wrestler.

25. Standing barbell lift off the rack hold behind neck is a super strength and tendon builder. I would do one-minute or 20-second holds. Really hits the back and traps hard.

26. The half block squat with extreme front lean really works the hips and lower back, and is a super strength builder.

27. Regular squat. Excellent power and strength builder; really good for lower leg strength.

28. The barbell squat is an excellent side-of-body power and coordination builder.

29. Excellent back, chest, and hamstring builder. Use as heavy and as big a rock as possible. Gets you used to supporting heavy bulk weight in front of the body.

30. Take barbell plate in one or both hands, with fingers underneath and thumb on top of plate, and curl. Excellent hand, wrist, finger, and thumb builder.

31. Builds superior wrist strength. Excellent training for boxers or street fighters.

32. A steel weight with a square-shaped round-bar handle is used. Place it between legs and lift up and down, one hand at a time. Excellent grip strength builder, along with lat, shoulder, biceps, and forearm.

33. Excellent grip builder; works all the muscles on the side of the body.

34. Builds tremendous coordination and strength in all the muscles that propel the body, especially the side muscles. Builds tremendous hand strength.

35. Builds super coordination and strength in all muscles that move the body. Works the side knee and ankles really hard.

36. Builds superior thumb strength as well as the forearm and triceps.

37. I would include the in-between kettlebell swing in the program of anybody who is serious about the art of super strength. It works so many muscle angles and builds grip coordination. Goerner used kettlebell swinging as his prime exercise, and Goerner was one of the strongest men in the world.

38. The two-hand kettlebell swing is a tremendous back builder. It hits the back dead center.

39. Builds tremendous toe strength, as well as side, hip, leg, stomach, and shoulder power. Indispensable movement for all who are in athletics because all power must start at the foot.

40. Smooth side out, weight plates are gripped with fingers and thumb. Builds hand, thumb, fingers, wrist, and top forearm strength.

41. Smooth side out, weight plates are squeezed together; lift from bench to chest high and hold for time. Builds tremendous crushing strength in the chest and builds forearm, biceps, and side elbow. Good movement for arm wrestlers. When plates are chest high, elbows should be down below the center of the plates.

42. Great hip, lower and upper back, and hamstring training; also good for training for rock and barrel lifting for strongmen.

43. Good for strengthening tendons and ligaments for all muscles used to pull weight from ground. Excellent for deadlift training.

44. Sledgehammer lifting in four positions, each hand, will build finger, hand, thumb, and wrist strength: thumb under handle, spin up from left to right; thumb under handle, spin from right to left; sledge to the front, whole hand grip, arm straight down along side of body—do front and back this way each hand.

45. The shovel lift is as described in this book works more muscles than almost any other single lift. Excellent lift for all-around strength from head to toe.

46. Builds tremendous grip. Use a dumbbell with a handle from 2-1/2" to 3" in diameter, or larger.

47. Builds superior neck strength.

48. This is just like the regular shovel lift, except you go clear over the head with the weight—front, side, back—while standing in a stationary position, without spinning. Really hits biceps and shoulder directly, and side and chest.

49. Builds superior shin strength, along with side, stomach, front, thigh, and hip power.

50. Builds superior side strength and strength throughout whole body.

51. Builds superior crushing grip power in hands.

52. Directly hits stomach, front, thighs, and shins.

53. Put barbell on two chairs or weight benches, crawl underneath in push-up position, lift off weight with the small of the back and hold. Builds strong stomach, chest, and arms tie-in. Good for wrestlers.

54. Pull weight above waist from floor and hold for time. Directly hits wrist, forearm, and biceps.

55. Lifting barbell with combinations of one and two fingers of each hand in different grips: reverse grip, thumb and forefinger grip, two little fingers, two front fingers. Builds tremendous grip strength.

56. Builds tremendous shoulder and upper body twisting power. Grab barbell off center so that the weight plate on one side is even with your face while the plate on the other side is clear over to the side of your body. Do each side.

57. Lifting with the shovel lift, pipe curl weight off floor a few inches and hold. Superior exercise for explosive upper body power and coordination.

58. Builds tremendous power throughout upper body. Good for boxers and baseballers, tennis, volleyball, and swimming.

59. Have a blacksmith make a steel brick with rounded edges, with a door on one end that bolts on so you can add weight. Builds tremendous punching power and arm strength for throwing. Good for boxers and baseballers, tennis, volleyball, and swimming.

60. Builds excellent power in hips, and coordination. These muscles should not be overlooked; they are very important.

61. Really hits the toes, calves, and front thighs hard and builds super coordination.

62. Superior movement to build wrestling and football strength; for hand-to-hand wrestling, builds superior thigh-to-body tie-in.

63. Builds excellent toe, calf, shin, front thigh, and hip strength.

64. Builds tremendous leg, hip and stomach strength.

65. Isometrics builds superior tone, speed, strength. They will really dig deep into the muscles and produce superior coordination and endurance holding strength.

66. These do the same as no. 65. It is good for any athlete once in a while to lock everything together to make everything work as a single unit.

67. Builds superior upper hip strength and coordination. Would be great for any footballer running back.

68. Builds power in both legs. A favorite of the sumo wrestlers in Japan.

69. Spinning side to side in full squat position with heavy barbell behind neck builds superior power in the side, ankles, side knee joints, side hips, and the inside of the legs, as well as good trunk twisting power. Would highly recommend for any wrestler or footballer. I do one set of 50 spins and afterward, I just throw the weight off my back and let it hit the floor behind me.

70. Lifting and just supporting weight in any position builds internal strength tie-in. Thirty second to one minute holds work the best.

71. Like step jumping, wall kicking, shoulder into wall smashing, and palm into telephone pole smashing for high reps builds good speed strength and power.

72. Any thick-handled barbell two inches or thicker builds superior grip strength.

73. Builds powerful hand, forearm, biceps, and wrist strength. Do high reps, like 50 to 100.

74. Builds powerful back, hips, shoulder and biceps strength.

75. Builds powerful hip, hamstring, and upper back strength.

76. Builds powerful back, hips, and shoulder. Builds good explosive power.

77. Another all-around lift builds tremendous power through the whole body from head to toe, and builds coordination and speed strength.

78. Builds whole upper body, strengthens stabilizer muscles, and makes back strong, also wrists, shoulders, and triceps.
79. Does the same as no. 76 with more upper body strengthening.
80. Builds explosive underload power. Teaches you how to explode under pressure; develops back, hip, shoulder, arm, and hamstring power.
81. Builds powerful traps, biceps wrist, chest, and shoulders.
82. Builds tremendous explosive power and coordination throughout whole body.
83. Builds tremendous cross-body wrenching power and coordination throughout the whole body.
84. Builds tremendous side wrenching power in arms, shoulders, and side muscles from head to toe.
85. Builds power in back and front of body, and triceps and forearm.
86. Builds tremendous front chest torque and works all side muscle tie-ins. Good exercise for explosive running power, especially in upper body.
87. Builds tremendous intestinal fortitude and endurance strength through whole body.
88. Builds superior jaw and neck strength.

CHAPTER 13

Gaining Strength at Any Age

I personally don't believe there are any limitations for gaining strength and endurance at any age—as long as you feel good and are healthy. For example, I saw a lady who was 70 years old run a 100-mile race through the Sahara Desert, and she didn't even start training till she was 62 years old. Now, I figure if she can run 100 miles through the sand in 120-degree temperatures at 70 years old, I shouldn't have any problem lifting weights for an hour at any age. I've also seen a picture of a guy that did a harness lift with a 2200-lb. dumbbell for 110 reps at 75 years old. Now you tell me if advanced age has hurt that guy any.

Anyone that has good health and says you're too old to lift and make good gains is just too lazy to try to do anything himself. I'm 40 years old and have been lifting for over 20 years, and I'm making gains faster now than when I was in my 20's. It's just a matter of will power, desire, work, eating well, and keeping a good mental attitude. Your mind will take your body anywhere it wants to go if you can see it in your mind's eye and believe in yourself.

The mind is so powerful when you believe. Look at George Foreman. He won the heavyweight boxing title at age 44, beating guys 20 years younger than himself in the ring. Look what Holyfield did to Tyson in the ring. They asked him how he did it and he said he believed that God gave him the faith to believe that he could do it. And he worked super hard because he believed he could do the impossible.

I know this cowboy named Duane Meister. He was Golden Gloves champ when he was younger. He's ridden in rodeos all around the country. He's had a lot of bones broken and worked hard all his life and can still outwork guys half his age, and he's about 44 years old now and still has a grip like a vise. He and I were talking one day about what good shape he was still in for his age. He told me a story of how one night he was in some bar out in western Nebraska and was in there drinking with this old farmer buddy of his. This guy was 65 years old and worked hard on the farm all his life.

Author Steve Justa at 40, getting stronger day by day.

Well, they were sitting there and in came a whole crew of construction workers feeling their oats, and for no reason picked a fight with the old man. Meister told me this old guy got up, ambled over there, and proceeded to mop the floor with the whole crew of those young construction workers. Then the old man just ambled back over to the table and all he said was, "I wonder what got into those boys," and just smiled. Now this guy was 65 years old, moved slow, talked slow; but when it came down to put up or shut up, he was as tough as nails.

From my own personal experience, I worked one summer building a highway bridge over the railroad tracks for a company called Beatrice Heavy Highway Construction. Half my crew consisted of guys over 60 years old, and we were working six ten-hour days every week for two months. Now, these guys over 60 had been doing this kind of work for over half their lives. I found out one thing and one thing quick—these characters were tough as nails physically and mentally.

Now, for all those who've never done bridge construction work, let me tell you it is backbreaking work ten hours a day, six days a week: digging trenches with shovels; busting rebar out of concrete with sledgehammers; carrying, laying and tying rebar; and a lot of drilling work, torch work, hammer work. Have you ever tried to bend over and tie rebar for ten hours a day? It is a killer, believe me.

And these so-called over-the-hill 60-year-old men were working my you-know-what into the dirt. For example, we had to knock over 2000 torched-off rivet bolts out of the swing joints in the beams with a sledgehammer and punch, standing on two 2 x 12 wooden boards in between the I-beams, 40 feet in the air. One slip and you've had it. Some of these rivet bolts took 15 minutes apiece to beat out, and some would come out in a minute, but we had 2000 of them to knock out. Well, my partner on this assignment was one of these 60-year-old guys, and it took him and me two days to knock all these bolts out, and I'll guarantee you, I took twice as many rest breaks as he did. The guy was tough as nails and I wasn't any slouch myself. I was 30 years old at the time, and here's this guy twice my age working my tail into the ground with backbreaking sledgehammer work.

So don't you never, ever let anybody get away with telling you you're too old to make good gains in strength or endurance. The power output of that sledgehammer work for ten hours would make the average weight training workout look like child's play, in terms of wear and tear on the body and in terms of hard work. I wish I had a dollar for every time somebody's told me I'm getting too old to lift weights or be strong. Every time I hear that I laugh to myself and shake my head and think, "take a hike, you idiot, you ain't got a clue."

Maybe in their minds I'm too old, but not in mine; and that's what counts — what's in your own mind. That is all that matters. If you want to do something bad enough and put all your heart and will into it, chances are you'll do it. The mind is more powerful than any supplement or vitamin; the mind is more powerful than physical age or testosterone level. Never, ever doubt the will of man; when challenged it can take you places you've never dreamed you'd go, and I don't care what age you are.

There was some guy a few years back that had a heavy chain vest on and he was 55 years old, and the TV reporter asked him how many Greyhound buses he was going to pull. His reply was, "Well, I pulled three when I was 50, so I think I'll be pulling four buses today for ya'll, now that I'm 55." This was on national TV. This is just another example, and I'm sure there are thousands more all around the world that you never hear about.

The old story is true for everybody, mentally and physically, "if you don't use it, you lose it." There is total truth in this saying. Now, I think the only difference between the older lifter and the younger lifter is if you don't use it, the faster you'll lose it; because in my mind, if you're not progressing, you'll be regressing. So keep moving forward.

CHAPTER 14

Personal Lifting Records

These are the lifts and endurance lifts I, the author, have personally done unofficially at one time or another in the last 15 years. A lot of them I can do better now, and a lot I can't do now; it's all a matter of what lifts I put more time into. But I give you these lifts as food for thought, just so you, the reader, can judge your own efforts against mine if you like.

I have always worked to develop an all-around strength and endurance. I hope you find these interesting; I know I always do when I read about peoples' personal records, no matter now big or how small. One thing I have learned about lifting over the years is there are hundreds of different kinds of bodily strength and endurance, and no one man will ever be the strongest in all of them at the same time; because there is always somebody out there who will outlift you in some form or another. There are over 600 different muscles in the body, and in one way or another, they are all important for doing something.

Steve Justa's personal weightlifting and endurance lifting records, performed at one time or another in the time frame of 1975 to 1996:

1. Truck push—4-ton truck, pushed the distance of 1/4 mile, one effort.
2. Back lift—3100 lb. for 35 reps, one set.
3. Railroad rail drag—backwards, with steel bar welded to the end of rail for hands to grip, 540 lb. for 1/8 mile, eight efforts in 25 minutes.
4. Railroad rail lift—ground to shoulder, carry on shoulder, 540 lb. for 30 feet, one set.

5. Steel 25-gal. barrel carry—ground to shoulder, 315 lb. for distance of 1/8 mile, one set. Barrel was about four feet tall.
6. Rock drag—570-lb. rock drag with chain by hands, 1/8 mile, 12 sets, 25 minutes.
7. Concrete rock lift—to chest from ground, 350 lb., 6 reps.
8. Wheel roll—425-lb. cast iron hay baler flywheel rolled and balanced by hand two miles on unlevel city streets, one set, 40 minutes. Flywheel was 2-1/2 inches wide and about three feet tall.
9. Concrete rock spin on end—570-lb. block about four feet tall with uneven end on the ground, for two blocks, 45 minutes on dirt surface.
10. Rock carry—220 lb. for distance of one mile in 1-1/2 hours.
11. Clean and jerk, squat style—300 lb., 1 rep.
12. Barbell reverse cheat curl—225 lb., 18 reps.
13. Barbell bench—400 lb., 1 rep.
14. Barbell deadlift carry—2"-thick solid steel bar from ground, walk 50 steps, 510 lb.
15. Dumbbell to shoulder overhead jerk—one hand, 175 lb.
16. Thick-handled dumbbell overhead jerk and press—one-hand, 135 lb. with 2-3/4-inch handle.
17. Three-quarter squat—500 lb., 30 reps, good front lean.
18. Half squat—800 lb., 20 reps.
19. Quarter squat—raise 1100 lb. off power rack, 50 reps.
20. Quarter squat - raise 1700 lb., hold 10 seconds, 1 rep.
21. Barbell deadlift carry—250 lb., one mile, 18 sets.
22. Negative deadlift—off rack to ground, 958 lb.
23. Deadlift off chairs and carry—700 lb., 20 steps backward, standard Olympic bar.
24. Barbell lift off rack—hold on shoulders behind neck, five minutes, one effort, 500 lb.
25. Barbell bench press—thick bar, top position lockout-hold from rack, 700 lb., 25 seconds.
26. Back lift and hold—3100 lb. for 45 seconds, 4500 lb. for 1 rep.

27. 30-gal. oil barrel lift—from ground to shoulder, 260 lb.
28. One-hand barbell lift off rack—elbow braced on stomach, free hand grabbing side of power rack, 500 lb., standing position, Olympic bar.

Steve Justa knocks out a few kettlebell swings.

29. Quarter squat raise off power rack—2000 reps in three hours, with 800 lb., total poundage lifted was 1,600,000 lb., a weight equivalent to 32 D7 Caterpillar bulldozers , or 16 fully-loaded semi-trucks and trailers, used sets of 20 reps.
30. Chain weight vest carry—carried a 200-lb. vest for two miles; weight was on back for a total of 50 minutes without a rest or leaning against anything. The hardest workout of one continuous effort without a rest I have ever endured.

31. Barbell half speed sprints—330-lb., 2-inch solid steel bar, 30 sets, for a distance of 50 steps each set, 1-1/4 hours.
32. Barbell carry behind neck—solid-steel bar with 700 lb., 50 sets of 20 steps each set, or a total distance of around one-half mile, two hours' time.
33. Barbell carry behind neck—800 lb. for 25 steps through the mud, with feet sinking up to the ankles in the mud at times. Most dangerous lift I ever did.
34. Kettlebell swing—200 lb. between legs to chest height, alternating hands in midair catch, 10 reps.
35. Hand and thigh lift, or quarter deadlift—using 7-1/2-foot, 1-1/2-inch diameter bar through the top of two 30-gal. oil barrels, one on each end. Barrels full of steel, 2050 lb., 1 rep up an inch off ground. 1300 lb. for 50 reps.
36. Bent press—145 lb. for 12 reps.
37. Chain vest truck wheel lift—weight in front of body, 2200-lb. wheel for 20 reps. Harness lift chain hooked from vest to the holes in the hub of wheel.
38. 16-gal. barrel of concrete, bear-hug walk—30 steps, 30 sets, 330-lb. barrel, one workout off waist-high stands.
39. Steel suitcase one-hand, one-side lift and carry—6 steps, 350 lb.
40. Shovel lift—210 lb., 5-foot pole, closest hand to the weight about 18 inches above weight. Weight was swung up to waist-level, then swung around behind the body, then back to front and set on ground.
41. Car front end sideways slide—back braced, one foot on wheel, one leg pushing, no help with hands. Front axle weight 1730 lb., slid sideways three inches.
42. Side shoulder raise—2-inch steel barbell off power rack with pad on shoulder, 1100 lb., 1 rep.
43. Barbell walk on shoulders—40 steps with 1200 lb. without wraps, suit or belt, just street clothes.
44. Standing barbell trunk twist—bar on shoulders, 600 lb., 30 reps.
45. Rock-bottom squat trunk twist—with barbell 500 lb., 20 reps.

46. Toe raise in rock-bottom squat position—with barbell 270 lb., 25 reps, then stand back up.
47. Frog walk—150 lb. for 50 steps in crouched position.
48. Wrist curl—135 lb. for 40 reps.
49. Stainless steel staff walk, alternating hands—Start with lifting shaft and walking, shaft held in vertical position with one arm until tired, then switching to other arm, back and forth, rotating arms, 14-mile stroll down railroad tracks with 30-lb. shaft.
50. Standing overhead press—225, 1 rep.
51. Two-arm front raise—vertical pipe with weight anchored on bottom, elbows half bent, 120 lb.
52. Hay bale throwing and stacking with hay hook—handled 1500 80-lb. hay bales every day for two weeks, seven days a week.
53. Two-man hay bale unload and stack—from truck to ground, 250 80-lb. bales in 20 minutes.
54. Two-arm front raise—elbows half-bent for endurance, with 8-foot long, 70-lb. shaft, for 500 reps in two hours.
55. Standard deadlift—Olympic bar, 330 lb. for 30 reps.
56. Deadlift off 8-inch block—700 lb. for 3 reps.
57. Chest squeeze—three 45-lb. plates, smooth side out, picked up off chair to chest, held 10 seconds with hands and wrists.
58. Weight plate finger curl—two hands, thumbs hooked on top, fingers underneath, 15 reps with 45-lb. plate.
59. Car tire spin—back braced, foot on car bumper, until tires spun one foot; rear axle weight 1700 lb., road surface was asphalt gravel mix. Held car to spin with one leg.
60. Jerk press to arm's length overhead and carry—250-lb., walk 100 steps.
61. One-hand kettlebell deadlift—between legs, round handle, off ground two inches, 500 lb., one rep. Endurance kettlebell 290 lb. off ground 300 reps in two hours.

62. Thick-handled barbell lift and carry—lift off rack, walk for distance behind neck, 240 lb. for 5-1/2 city blocks, one effort; hand, wrist and forearm tired long before body power, so had to drop the weight in 5-1/2 blocks.
63. Three-quarter good morning—500 lb. for 20 reps.